Praise for *Meeting Amazing Grace*

"*Meeting Amazing Grace* captivated me like my favorite novels, yet left me wiser, more hopeful, more sure of the principles for loving and supportive family interaction. I highly recommend this book."
　　—**Darla Isackson,** writer, editor, mother, grandmother

"I love this book! I'm buying it for all my children, and will be reviewing it in the three book clubs of which I belong."
　　—**Shawna Powelson,** author, mother of eight

"I think *Meeting Amazing Grace* should be required reading for every young couple! It is just outstanding. And it is so much fun to read because it is presented in such an interesting and entertaining way. Knowing that these stories really happened certainly adds to the authority of the messages. One of the stories of forgiveness brought tears to my eyes. I think some of the most important teachings were the ones on setting boundaries. It's hard to do, but makes a world of difference."
　　—**Bonnie Murray,** songwriter, mother in Colorado

"Relationships can be complex. Families need a guide, and *Meeting Amazing Grace* provides the needed help in a fun, easy to read style. I highly recommend this book."
　　—**Thomas B. Holman,** Ph.D., School of Family Life, Brigham Young University

"I've never underlined a book this much since I was in college. I absorbed it into my very soul. I haven't been this engrossed in a book for a very long time. And it's so fun to read."
　　—**Marie Spencer**, retired school teacher

"Another insightful, helpful book from the Lundbergs. Well done!"
　　—**Thomas E. Myers, MD**, family practice physician

"I like this book. The Lundbergs show that the secret is not just patience and forgiveness but gratitude for the good that is in the family that, after all, raised the spouse you love."

—**Steven E. Rhoads, Ph.D.**, University of Virginia, author of *Taking Sex Differences Seriously*

"I just finished reading *Meeting Amazing Grace*. I'm a Louis L'Amour kind of guy, but I was captivated by this book. I don't usually cry reading books, but I did in this one. Most important, I found helpful ideas for my own family. Thank you so much."

—**Darrell Saunders**, businessman, father in Utah

"I learned so much so painlessly. It's like a spoonful of sugar."

—**Janice Moyle**, mother-in-law in training

"This beautifully written novel inspires the reader to seek an understanding of those who become a major part of our lives through marriage—in-laws. The insights Gary and Joy Lundberg share make it easy to open the windows and doors of the soul to truly love our increased family circle with all our heart."

—**James Michael Pratt**, NY Times best-selling author of *The Last Valentine*

"I found *Meeting Amazing Grace* to be both validating and enlightening. It is the perfect gift for anyone who doesn't already have it."

—**Sandy Willis**, mother of 4 sons in Virginia

"I loved Grandma Grace's invaluable advice! It's not just about mothers and fathers-in-law, but far more than that. It has helped me so much. Thank you!"

—**Elizabeth Loderup,** wife and mother in Texas

"I welcome this wonderful source of light on in-law relationships. In this up-beat book, familiar problems-in-process are shared with humor, realistic positive examples, and optimism. This book is delightful!"

—Shirley Cox, Ph.D., former President of The National
Association of Social Workers

"I finished your book and then bought 13 more for family, friends, and two for wedding gifts. They have to have this book!"

—Debi Hobson, college student, mother, grandmother

"I love the stories and the style. Perfect for my clients."

—Susan Gilbert, marriage and family therapist
in Nevada

"What a marvelous book. Not only is it enjoyable reading, it is a good refresher course in basic human communication — whether the humans be in-laws or not. Although many of the stories revolve around extremely serious life issues, they are told in a way that engenders hopeful, positive emotions in the reader. Your writing will, once again, strengthen families beyond anything you can ever imagine."

—Melany Wilkins, social worker, mother, grandmother

"If every couple would read *Meeting Amazing Grace* they would have the compassion, love, kindness, understanding, and patience to fully love their spouse, children, and in-laws. Imagine how grand life would be!"

—Koko Cardiff, school teacher, single mother

MEETING AMAZING
Grace

Other Books by Gary & Joy Lundberg

I Don't Have to Make Everything All Better

Married For Better Not Worse

On Guard

MEETING AMAZING
Grace

Wisdom for all Families and In-Laws
A novel based on true stories

Gary & Joy Lundberg

Riverpark
PUBLISHING

Riverpark Publishing Company
7550 No. 145th East Avenue
Owasso, OK 74055
1-800-224-1606

Cover design by Jana Parkin

Manufactured in the United States of America

Library of Congress Control Number: 2008927832

ISBN 10: 0-915029-06-5
ISBN 13: 987-0-915029-06-8

Contents

Authors' Note

*D*ear Reader,

Through the means of the supernatural you are about to embark on an unusual path of discovery with an amazing woman named Grace. You may be pleasantly surprised to find solutions to your own challenges as you step into the lives of families facing dramatic, yet all-too-common, dilemmas. It will be as if you have a crystal ball showing you what can be done to bring peace and love between you and your own family members and in-laws. You will see how the clashing of personalities and differing family traditions and beliefs can be transformed into loving, rich relationships.

If you sense a realism about these encounters, even the most bizarre, it's because all are based on true experiences of real people.

Gary and Joy Lundberg

Chapter One
Window of Understanding

$\mathscr{T}$he lights in the restaurant were dim, allowing the candle on their table to create a soft glow that highlighted Jeff's features in a way that made Lindsey's heart skip a beat. They came here often to enjoy the cozy atmosphere while indulging in delicious pasta.

"That was the best seafood alfredo yet," Jeff said, wiping his lips with his napkin.

"Yeah, it was," said Lindsey. "Thanks for sharing. And my linguine wasn't bad either."

"Not bad at all," he said.

She liked how his dark hair had a touch of curl in it, cut just right, not too short and not too long—professional enough looking but still slightly whimsical. The style complemented the dimple in his right cheek, which made its appearance whenever he smiled even the slightest bit.

"I'm glad things are going well for you at work, Lindsey," Jeff said, the dimple appearing. Then leaning closer he said,

"I hope they know how lucky they are to have someone like you working for them."

"I don't know about that, but I do know I'm lucky to have a job I enjoy so much."

"I know what you mean," he said, "It feels good, doesn't it?"

Being with Jeff was easy. He was much more than just a fun date. They could talk about anything and everything. Besides that he treated her with more respect and kindness than any guy she'd ever dated, not that she was dating anyone else lately. Jeff had pretty much risen to the top.

As she reached for her glass to take another sip, he took hold of her hand. Placing his other hand on top of it, he looked deep into her eyes and said, "Lindsey, do you have any idea what a truly beautiful woman you are?"

She blushed, then lowered her eyes,

"Why, thank you, Jeff. You're not so bad yourself."

"I'm not talking flattery here, Lindsey. I sincerely mean it. You're beautiful, from head to toe, inside and out. And every minute I spend with you makes me happy. I'm hoping with all my heart that it's working both ways."

She smiled and said, "Yes, I'd say it's definitely working both ways." Her heart started beating faster.

"Well, I . . . uh . . . thought maybe . . ." he hesitated slightly and at that moment his cell phone vibrated.

"Excuse me," he said. Letting her hand go he pulled out his phone, looked at the caller ID, and said, "I need to take this one." Then back into the phone, "Hi, Mom. Are you okay?"

Lindsey's heart sank, her concerns once again confirmed. After a few minutes he said goodbye and hung up. He reached for Lindsey's hand again.

She resisted and reached for her purse instead. "It's getting late and I've still got some work to do on an assignment. I think we better call it a night."

Helping her with her coat, he said, "I think I need to get rid of my cell."

"Your phone is not the problem," she said, then walked toward the door.

❀❀❀

Mondays were always busy at Success Marketing. It was as if a world of panic-stricken clients waited for the clock to strike 9:00 AM, each hoping that the weekend had brought the perfect, brilliant idea that would sell their product to millions of eager buyers. Lindsey thrived on the creativity this pressure stimulated, but in her three years with the company she had learned the value of taking some time away from the stress. Even a few minutes break could refresh her, renew her perspective. It was like stepping outside and looking at everything through a window. She once told Jeff, "There are things you can see more clearly when you aren't there in the room."

Lindsey was sitting alone in the break room sipping at her peppermint tea. Even just the aroma was stress-relieving. The clicking of high heels entered the room and her moment of peace vanished.

"What a morning!" said Olivia, filling her cup from the coffee machine and plopping in the chair next to Lindsey. "It's like a beehive around here today,"

"That's for sure. It's going to be a relief to get away for a few days," said Lindsey.

"Oh, that's right, you're going to the conference. When are you leaving?"

"My plane takes off at nine tomorrow morning."

Olivia cut her chocolate covered donut in half. "Here, Lindsey, help me out. Deliver me from at least half of my temptation."

"Thanks. I could use a little brain food," she said, taking a big bite. "It's going to be a great conference. Some of the best advertising geniuses in the country will be there. I'm looking forward to it, and to a break from . . . well, everything," Lindsey said.

"Everything? Sounds like more than just the office."

"I need to get away and clear my head."

Lindsey had confided in Olivia before. Olivia had a good listening ear but it had one frailty, it was attached to a loose tongue. She relished rattling off her opinions on almost any subject, particularly personal problems—hers and everyone else's.

"When are you going to stop dating this guy? That's the problem, isn't it?" Olivia said with a tone of disgust. "You're getting in over your head, Lindsey."

"No I'm not. Jeff's a wonderful guy."

"How wonderful can a guy be when he's tethered to a controlling mother? Hey, I've listened to the stories you've told me and I'm certain you're going to regret going further with this relationship. He's owned, Lindsey. Don't you get it? It's going to be like walking around with Mr. Tall, Dark and Handsome, with you on one arm and his mother desperately hanging onto the other."

"That's not nice, Olivia."

"Well, living with him won't be so nice, either. I'm just trying to open your eyes. Look, I know what I'm talking about. Believe me, it's no picnic being married to a man who is also married to his mother. If you married Jeff, I'd give you, oh, maybe two years at the most."

"Olivia, that's terrible. Anyway, he hasn't even asked me yet."

"Consider yourself lucky. Next time I get married I'm going to marry a man who grew up alone on a deserted island."

"Oh, I can see him now," Lindsey laughed, "in his loin cloth swinging on a vine with a half peeled banana in his other hand. Now that's a formula for a happy marriage."

"What can I say? My ex-mother-in-law was a doozie. You think I'm going to jump into that cesspool again? Uh uh. No way. If I remain single for the rest of my life it will be far better than what I just bailed out of."

"Hey, did I hear someone say ex-mother-in-law?" It was Larry, jumping in uninvited. "And what would you know about in-laws?" Olivia challenged.

"See this ring on my finger? I know plenty." With cup in hand he pulled up a chair and joined them. "So what's the deal?"

"No deal," said Lindsey. "Just talking."

"Well, let me give you a bit of advice. When you get married . . ."

"*If* I get married," Lindsey said.

"Okay. *If* you get married, here's what you do. Move at least a thousand miles away from both parents and you'll be just fine. That's what we did after the first butting-in session from my wife's mother. I could see the handwriting on the wall."

"And," Lindsey said, "is your wife happy about that decision?"

"I think she's pretty happy to be away from *her* in-laws. But not so happy to be away from her own parents. In fact, she's pretty unhappy about that part."

"And how about you, Larry," Olivia said. "Are you happy?" She knew the answer.

"Sure, I'm happy. At least happy I'm away from my interfering in-laws."

"And happy to be away from your own parents?" Lindsey questioned.

"Not exactly. I miss playing golf with my dad," he said a little melancholy. "But if that's the price for peace then so be it."

"There has to be a better way," Lindsey said, troubled by the whole idea of having to move away from her family.

"There is a better way: my way. Stay single," Olivia said. Then checking her watch. "I've gotta get back to work."

"Me, too," said Lindsey, eager to be out of this conversation and all the hard questions it posed in her already troubled mind.

As she stood to leave Larry said, "But there is one good thing about this in-law thing.

That caught Lindsey's attention. "Like what?"

"I got a terrific brother-in-law out of the deal. He's become one of my best friends. Truth be known, he's the reason we chose to move here, to be away from you-know-who and closer to him and his wife. So it's not all bad."

"Well, on that slightly more positive note," Lindsey said, "I'll see you all later."

❀❀❀

In bed that night, with the quilt pulled up almost over her head, all Lindsey could think of was what Olivia had said. The words, "tethered to his mother" kept going through her mind. She never should have told Olivia about the time Jeff's mother got upset at her for inviting him to that concert on the very day of his mother's birthday. Jeff had said, "Oh, she won't mind. I'll take her to dinner the next day." Well, she did mind because she had her own plans, and they didn't include Lindsey. Then there was the time she told Olivia that his mother told him he was spending too much time with Lindsey and not enough with her.

"What does Olivia know," she rationalized in her head. *"She hasn't even met Jeff. If she really knew him . . ."*

And then there was Larry's stupid advice. Right out loud she said, "I'm not moving far away from my parents just so Jeff, or some future husband, won't have to deal with them." Her mind was on a roll. *And as far as getting anything out of it, Jeff doesn't even have a sibling for me to be friends with. But then, I do have some who could be his . . . if they happen to get along, and who knows if that'll happen. Oh, this is too complicated!*

She groaned and pulled the pillow over her head trying to close out the flood of thoughts that wouldn't leave her alone. After an hour of tossing and turning, she finally got up and fixed a cup of warm milk, hoping that would relax her mind. She needed a good night's rest to be fresh for the trip and the demanding schedule of the conference.

After slowly sipping the milk she went back to bed and finally fell asleep, tossing and turning until the alarm went off.

She showered and quickly dressed for the trip. A knock at the door let her know that Jeff had arrived to pick her up. She could have taken a taxi, but he insisted on driving her to the airport. At the curb side check in he helped with her bags, gave her a kiss and handed her a package.

"Don't open it until you get to your hotel."

"What is it?" Lindsey said.

"A surprise. We'll talk about it when you get home." He kissed her again, jumped back into his car and waved as he drove away. Puzzled, she waved back and put the package, which was about the size of a book, into her carry-on bag, and off she went to the gate.

After checking into the hotel Lindsey opened the package. It was definitely a surprise. And it wasn't a book. She gave it her full attention for the next thirty minutes then had to leave for the conference.

❀❀❀

The next four days were packed full. The conference had been everything Lindsey had anticipated it would be, exhilarating and exhausting, filled with non-stop workshops and networking. And now it was over. Her head was filled with new ideas, but not enough to crowd out the overwhelming presence of a decision she had to make, a decision that would affect the rest of her life.

She took a cab to the hotel and dropped off her laptop and conference things. Needing to clear her head she decided to go for a walk. She changed into a comfortable sweater and jeans, and then stopped before leaving the room, deciding to take another look at Jeff's surprise. That done, she headed again for the door, convinced even more that she needed the walk. Tomorrow she would go home and she wasn't really ready for that yet. She would liked to have had a few more days away. But if she stayed in the hotel she knew she would only sit there and stew about what Jeff had given her. *"Get outside, get some perspective,"* she told herself. *"Look at it from the outside."*

Her walk was much longer and farther than planned. She was attracted to a narrow street of quaint Victorian row houses. The small yards were adorned with patches of neatly trimmed grass and carefully designed English-style flowering gardens with decorative stone walkways intertwined. It was a lovely setting.

A unique park bench at the edge of the sidewalk seemed to invite her to sit and enjoy the scene. She was ready for a rest. The bench was made of wooden slats with a back high enough to rest her head and a seat that caused her to sit back in a most comfortable position. She made a mental note that someday she needed to have one of these, nestled in her own English garden. She loved flowers, and a place to sit while she enjoyed them.

Sitting there relaxed on the bench Lindsey closed her eyes and silently prayed to know what to do. She had been wrestling with her dilemma all week, and long before that. Overcome by exhaustion she drifted off to sleep.

When she opened her eyes she noticed a small sign on the door of one of the houses and walked over for a closer look. It said, "Grandma Grace." Below were the words "Visitors Welcome." On the door was a decorative brass knocker. She felt drawn to it and lifted her hand to knock, then pulled away, thinking it odd to be knocking on a stranger's door for no reason at all, except curiosity. What would she even say if someone answered. A force beyond her own drew her back to the knocker, and before she knew it she was knocking on the door.

She waited a few seconds, then, somewhat relieved, turned to walk away when she heard the door open.

"Don't go," said the old woman. "I've been expecting you." She gestured for Lindsey to enter.

"Are you Grandma Grace?" Lindsey asked tenuously, feeling compelled to step inside.

"Just like the sign says. And you are Lindsey Powers."

"How did you know?" She was shocked.

The old woman just smiled and took Lindsey's hand with her soft, warm, wrinkled one and gently led her into her parlor. It had to be a parlor. Parlors are filled with memory trinkets, old photos and crocheted afghans on the furniture. A charming old Tiffany lamp with beads edging the shade warmed the room with soft colorful light. Beside it was a vase of fresh picked yellow daisies. A large Bible, obviously well used, lay open on the coffee table.

On a small desk in the corner of the room was a strange looking computer. The idea of a computer in this antique-filled room seemed paradoxical. It had a large flat screen with flashing lights down one side. Wild flowers literally danced across the screen. The keyboard was unlike any she'd ever seen, with symbols unfamiliar to her. When she stepped into Grandma Grace's house she had felt like she was going back in time, but now she felt like she was seeing the future.

"Is that a computer?" Lindsey asked to be sure.

"Yes, top of the line, and I know how to use it. Comes in real handy in my line of work," she said. "Wanna see?"

"Sure, I guess."

Grandma Grace went to the keyboard, clicked on one of the keys and suddenly on the screen appeared the back view of a bride wearing a magnificent white satin gown with a white floral design embroidered down a train that spread majestically onto the floor. The bride's dark hair was swept up in the back into a cluster of curls with a shoulder-length veil flowing from beneath.

"Oh, my goodness, what a beautiful gown!" Lindsey said, captivated by the scene.

The old woman jotted a note on a small piece of paper. "Here's the website. You may want to visit this site again some day." She tucked the paper in Lindsey's pocket. Then she pushed another key and the bride became three dimensional, appearing to swirl out of the screen and onto the desk as she turned gracefully around to show the front of the gown.

"That's amazing," Lindsey said, stunned by the technology. Then she saw the bride's face, and gasped. "That's me! What's going on? What's happening?"

"Sorry. I couldn't resist having a little fun. I think you'll make a beautiful bride, that's all." She clicked again and the bride was gone. "I just love what this computer can do and couldn't resist showing it off to you." The wild flowers were back dancing on the screen.

Lindsey was speechless. She didn't know what to say. She couldn't get her bearings and wondered what she was doing here. Her eyes went back to the old woman to examine her for a clue as to who she was. Her round face with its warm smile and hint of blush could easily be classified as charming and even cute. Slightly on the plump side, she looked to be about five feet plus a couple of inches tall. She was wearing a wispy sky-blue dress with a skirt that swayed when she walked, hitting just above her ankles, revealing low-heeled shoes. Draped around her shoulders was a white fringed shawl that matched her short, slightly tousled white hair. Her appearance gave no clue as to her identity except that she was on the feminine, yet practical, side of fashion.

Ignoring Lindsey's obvious scrutiny of her, the old woman walked to the sofa, sat down and patted the seat next to her, inviting Lindsey to sit.

"So, you're getting married," Grandma Grace said. It wasn't a question; it was a statement of fact.

"Well, I don't know . . ." Lindsey started and then stopped. "Who are you?" she asked incredulously.

"Someone who cares about you," said the old woman. "Just like you, I'm here on assignment."

"On assignment?"

"Let's not worry about that. I'll just say my boss has been listening to you. Now back to the facts, so you're getting married," she said with a knowing smile.

"It's not a fact. I may or may not be getting married. Frankly, I'm scared to death about it," Lindsey said looking down at her knees, and noticed they were quivering.

"Yes, I know. Are you cold, Lindsey? Here this will help." She took the afghan that was draped over the arm of the sofa.

"No. No I'm not cold." She did not want to be wrapped in an crocheted afghan.

"So what's the problem?" said Grandma Grace, putting the afghan back.

Lindsey took a deep breath. "Oh, I don't know. It's not Jeff. He's the best guy any woman could ever want for a husband. We've been dating for a little over a year now, so I really do know him well. He treats me . . ."

". . . like a queen," Grandma Grace said.

Her face was gentle, with deep creases that spoke of a long and hard life. Her eyes were penetrating, yet filled with compassion and a twinkle that led Lindsey to believe she could trust her. It felt natural to be with her, like she'd known her for a long time.

"It's not Jeff, Grandma Grace," she repeated.

"Call me G. G."

"Gigi?"

"That works."

"Jeff's a hardworking guy and has only three months left before he graduates with a master's degree in animation. And he has a great part-time job at the studio, so you can see he's ambitious. And, Grandma Grace . . . uh, Gigi, he's so fun to be with. He really knows how to make me laugh. I love being with him."

"He makes me laugh, too."

"You know him?" She was totally surprised

"I know he asked you to marry him . . . Disney style."

"It was so cute," Lindsey said. "He made a short—very short—animated DVD. I didn't really know what it was because he handed it to me in a package when he dropped me off at the airport for this trip. He kissed me goodbye and told me not to open it until I got to the hotel. Then he said we'd talk about it when I returned home. As soon as I got there I played it. It shows this adorable little monkey, more appealing than any cartoon monkey I've ever seen—he's gifted, Gigi," she smiled proudly. "Well, anyway the monkey is holding a crystal platter with a silver domed lid on it, like it was some kind of gourmet dish. The monkey does a little dance and sings . . . want to hear it?" She said a little embarrassed, like she'd gone too far.

"Course I do."

"Okay, here goes." By now she knew it well, she'd played it at least a dozen times. She began singing, "Hey, Lindsey, cutest girl in town, we could have a lot of fun monkeyin' around. So how about goin' bananas with me, not just for now but for all e-ter-ni-teee," She ended with the same drama as the monkey. "Then off comes the silver dome and there's a diamond ring on the plate! A diamond ring!"

"Very cute. And your answer will be?"

"Oh, Gigi, I do love him. I want to say yes. But, it's not that easy. I'm really worried about something. It's not him . . it's . . . it's . . ."

". . . his mother. Sarah McKinsey Sloan," Gigi said with that knowing tone in her voice that Lindsey was becoming acquainted with.

"You know about her?"

"I don't just know *about* her, I *know* her. And you need to know her, too."

"Oh, I know her alright. That's what makes it all so frightening. I love Jeff with all my heart. He's just about everything I've ever wanted in a husband, but I'm afraid our marriage will be ruined by his mother. She's nice enough, I guess, it's just that she's so . . . so . . . into his life. And Jeff is really devoted to her. I've heard too many horror stories at work about meddling in-laws. One of my co-workers got divorced recently and she lays it at the feet of her mother-in-law. I don't want that to happen to me, Gigi. I want to be married. I want a husband, I just don't want a mother-in-law."

She chuckled. "I don't think that's possible, unless, of course, you marry an orphan. The problem is you love Jeff and he's not an orphan."

"If Jeff even has the sniffles, she's right there with homemade chicken noodle soup. If he doesn't call her every day her feelings are hurt. If he ever forgot her birthday she'd cry for days on end, and would probably blame me for it. What will she do when we have children? Want them named after her, no doubt. She'll want me to raise them exactly like she raised Jeff. She'll be over every day telling me how to cook, how to clean, how to change a diaper, how to . . ."

"Shhhhh," she put her finger to Lindsey's lips. "Take my hand." They walked over to the computer. Gigi touched one of the keys and clicked it quickly three times.

❀❀❀

The next thing Lindsey knew she and Gigi were standing in a hospital room. On the bedside stand was a bouquet of pink and white roses, filling the room with their fragrance. In the bed lay a woman connected to an IV and monitoring wires. From the gaunt and sunken look on her face, she appeared to be near death, and much too young to die. A young man who appeared to be in his late twenties was tenderly holding her hand. A little girl about six years old was stroking her cheek. The man gently picked up the little girl and placed her on his lap so she could be closer to the woman. The child leaned down near the woman's face, her tears dropped softly on the woman's cheek.

"Don't die, Mommy," the little girl said, her small cheek touching her mother's. "Please don't die."

Barely able to talk, the mother whispered to her child, "Be a good girl for Daddy."

"I will Mommy. Don't die, please." The little girl started crying softly as she laid her head on her mother's shoulder, nestling as close as she could.

The father gently patted his little daughter's back in an effort to comfort her. At the same time his other hand was holding his wife's limp hand. He was doing his best to comfort them both.

Lindsey was visibly shaken and saddened by what she was seeing. Her thoughts raced to her own mother and how devastated she would be without her, even now as a grown woman. Mothers hold a private, permanent place in a child's heart, no matter the age.

"Oh, Gigi, I hope she doesn't die. Who is she?"

Gigi simply smiled and turned toward the scene.

The mother looked at her child and with her last ounce of strength whispered, "I . . . love . . . you, . . . little Sarah."

"Sarah? Did she say Sarah?" Lindsey said in astonishment.

"Yes. Sarah. The little girl is Jeff's mother. Now look at the monitor."

A flat line appeared on the screen. "Oh, no! I don't want her mother to die," she said, as if what she wanted mattered.

Suddenly the room was filled with nurses and doctors, but it was too late. The woman was gone. The father picked up little Sarah and tenderly held her in his arms, comforting her as best he could while obviously suffering his own deep sorrow.

"Oh, Gigi, this is too sad," she said, turning her head away, almost wishing she hadn't seen it.

"There is something else you need to see," Gigi said. "Take my hand."

❀❀❀

In an instant they were in a cemetery. It was a beautiful peaceful place, green and well-cared for, with tall pines dotting the landscape. A small pond with lily pads and a few ducks was nearby. It was a lovely place for the living to come and pay tribute to their departed loved ones. Several yards from the pond a woman of about thirty or so was placing a flower on a grave stone. A young boy, about five years old dressed in jeans and a Superman tee shirt, was at her side. It appeared from the growth that the grave had been there for a couple of years. They seemed to be the only ones there.

"He was a good daddy, wasn't he, Mama," said the boy.

"The best. But the really best part is, I still have you, and you're such a good boy, just like your daddy," said the woman.

At that moment the boy caught sight of a squirrel and dashed off to chase it.

The mother smiled and ran after the boy, shouting, "Wait for me, Jeffie!"

Lindsey gasped as her hand went to her mouth in astonishment. "That's Jeff when he was a little boy!"

"Watch," Gigi said.

The mother ran with the boy as he chased the squirrel. It ran up a tall pine tree and they both fell to the ground laughing. She tickled the boy and he jumped up and ran away again. She ducked behind a large head stone where he couldn't see her.

"Okay, where are you, Mama?" He went creeping playfully from one headstone to the next. When he got close she jumped out and said "Boo!" He laughed and threw his arms around her and off they went to the car.

"She loves him so much," Lindsey said, deeply touched by what she had just seen.

"She'd give her life for him," Gigi said. "And that's basically what she's done."

"Her life must have been hard," Lindsey said. "She lost too many close loved ones in her young years—first her mother, then her husband. How terribly difficult that must have been for her." The window was opening and so was her heart.

"Indeed it was difficult," Gigi said. "Come with me."

❀❀❀

The words on the door said State Employment Services. Sarah, dressed in a neatly pressed light blue blouse and dark skirt, sat in front of a desk where she was being interviewed. She held her hands tightly together to keep from wringing them.

"I'm sorry, but you don't have the right qualifications," said the interviewer, looking at Sarah over his reading glasses. "You need an education in order to have a job that would pay the salary you're asking for."

"But I have a child to care for. I need something now."

"I'm sorry," he said sympathetically. He jotted some information on a piece of paper and handed it to her. "Here are a few jobs you could try until something better comes along."

They followed her for the next few days. She finally found a job doing housekeeping for a small motel.

"It was all she could find that would allow her to have time to attend college," Gigi said. "She qualified for a grant that paid the tuition. So while Jeffie was in school she worked and went to classes. A kind neighbor watched him for the extra two hours until she got home. After a hard day of work and classes she cared for her son, did the household chores, then studied. It was a grueling schedule and at the end of each day she literally collapsed into bed."

"I had no idea she'd gone through so much. I knew a little of her story, Gigi, but not the heart of it. It just didn't register with me before. I never knew the sacrifices she made to become a school teacher. All she said was that it was a good occupation so she could be on Jeff's schedule. She's never complained to me about what she went through. I didn't know."

"What we don't know about a person keeps us from understanding them," Gigi said. "Our perception changes when the window of our understanding is opened."

"No wonder she treats him with such loving care. But how do I deal with that? She's smothering him. She'll never let him go. I don't want to hurt her, but this could be a big problem for me if I marry Jeff. Now I understand why she's the way she is, but it doesn't solve the problem."

"No, but it's a beginning. Keep this Pertinent Point in mind: knowing the heartaches of an in-law's past can help you love them in the present. Now hold on."

Lindsey grabbed Gigi's hand tightly and off they went, swishing through time and space.

Chapter Two
Window of a Listening Heart

They were at a park in a canyon. Dozens of people were all over the place, women sitting on folding chairs chattering away, men studying each other's every move as they played an intense game of horseshoes, teenagers having fun playing volleyball and smaller children laughing as they threw rocks into a nearby stream trying to bomb their stick boats. Tables covered with red and white checkered paper tablecloths held a variety of unmatched dishes loaded with salads, baked beans, fried chicken, rolls and numerous other goodies just waiting to be eaten.

"This has to be a family reunion," Lindsey said.

"You don't know any of these people, Lindsey, and neither does Jeff. It's not your family, but it's a family that deals with its own struggle, and you can learn from them. See the woman on the end over there?"

"The one with the graying hair, there in the pink shirt?"

"Yes. Her name is Helen and she's talking to her daughter-in-law, Marianne. Something significant is happening between the two of them at this very moment. But you can't possibly understand the importance of it unless you have a glimpse of what's gone on for the past twenty years."

In a blink they were at a wedding. Bouquets of white carnations on white wrought iron stands lined the aisle. A minister and a handsome groom in a black tux stood in front of a candle-lit background. The audience was seated as they awaited the bridal procession. Then the familiar strains of *Here Comes the Bride* rang from the organ's pipes and everyone rose to their feet. The groom's face brightened as he saw his radiant bride walking up the aisle on the arm of her father. A new family was about to be created. The feeling was electric.

"Marianne makes a beautiful bride, don't you think, Helen?" whispered the groom's father to his wife as they watched the procession.

"Yes, but I wish she would have pulled her hair back. I hate how it hangs in her eyes most of the time."

"Yes, but . . . yes, but . . . yes, but. Do you always have to say 'yes, but' to everything? Can't you ever just say 'yes' and let that be enough?"

"John, you're impossible. I can never carry on a decent conversation with you anymore."

"Okay, okay. Shhhhh. Let's not get into another argument, especially at Ryan's wedding. I think Marianne looks beautiful, and that's that."

"Fine. She looks beautiful. Are you happy now?"

"Why are you showing me this, Gigi? Is my mother-in-law going to resent me right from day one? I don't think I want to see this."

"Patience, my dear, have a little patience. That's the problem with most people. They want everything neatly tied up and solved immediately, and that's as likely to happen as having a baby born fully clothed, potty trained and carrying a how-to manual. Life isn't like that. Relationships take time. Watch how this one unfolds."

They went quickly from scene to scene through the past twenty years as Helen interacted with John, Ryan, Marianne and other members of her family. Poor Helen. She was continually finding fault and complained endlessly about her hard life, and it appeared that nobody was one whit interested in the continual barrage. Lindsey could only think what a miserable in-law this woman would be and hoped never to have one like her.

Finally, they were in Helen's kitchen where she and Marianne were cleaning up after a family dinner. Other family members were in the nearby living room, laughing and enjoying being together.

"My body's falling apart inch by inch, Marianne," Helen complained, as usual. "You know the problem I've been having with my eyes; well, I went to the doctor yesterday and he said I have cataracts that need to be removed. I don't know what to do. I'm scared."

Trying to be encouraging to her mother-in-law, Marianne said, "You should do it, Mom. Cataract surgery used to be hard and dangerous, but not nowadays. It's no big deal anymore. You just go in and get them painlessly removed by a laser."

"Maybe it's no big deal to you. It's not your eyes. You don't know what might happen during the surgery. I could end up blind."

"That just never happens. Stop worrying so much."

Helen burst into tears, threw down the dish towel and ran out of the kitchen mumbling, "Nobody cares about what I'm going through. Nobody."

Ryan came in, "What's going on, Marianne?"

"Ryan, I'm sorry, but your mother's impossible. There's no way I can talk to her."

A few days later they were with Marianne in her own home. She was listening to the radio as she prepared baked beans for the family reunion.

"There's a simple solution to most troubled relationships," said the radio voice.

"I know that voice," said Lindsey. "Is that you, Gigi?"

"Shhhh. Can't learn a thing if your mouth's in gear."

"Most people just need to be listened to," said the voice. "How do you feel when you pour your heart out to someone and they interrupt by telling you what you should do? Or how about when you're feeling bad about something and they say, 'Hey, life's not so bad. You've got a roof over your head and food on the table.' How fun is that to hear when you're feeling down about something? Makes you want to smack the person right in the nose, doesn't it?"

"Gigi, that *is* you!"

"Listen up, Lindsey."

Marianne stopped working on the beans and went straight to the radio. She sat down, moved closer and listened intently.

"Most people don't want to be told what to do," the voice said. "They just need someone to listen to them. They need to be validated, not reprimanded, instructed, or cheered up. Just listened to and understood. That's what shows genuine caring and respect. Put yourself in their shoes and try to understand from their point of view."

The light went on inside of Marianne. Right out loud she said, "My mother-in-law is not the problem, I am!"

"No, no, no! She's wrong, Gigi. Her mother-in-law *is* the problem," Lindsey said.

"My oh my, you're quick to make a judgment." Gigi rolled her eyes.

"Quick? What do you mean quick? I've just seen twenty years of her whining."

"Listen to the radio," Gigi said.

"Let me explain how this works by sharing an experience of a woman I'll call Julie and her daughter-in-law Taylor. Not their real names, of course—gotta protect the guilty. On with the story," said the radio voice. "Julie's son, Todd, had been called up for a one-year tour of duty in the military and since he and Taylor had a six-month-old baby boy, Julie invited them to come and live with her while he was gone. There was room since she had only one child still at home, a fifteen-year-old daughter, Tara. Living with them would allow Taylor to save

rent and she wouldn't have to seek employment and could be home to care for their baby. Julie thought this would be a good chance to help them out while developing a closer relationship with her grandson and daughter-in-law.

"Julie worked as a teacher at the local elementary school and when she came home from work she was usually well spent. One day, after a particularly exhausting day, she heard Taylor crying in her room. Since there was always an underlying fear that her son would be wounded or killed, that was her first terrifying thought. Here's how the dialogue went.

" 'What's wrong? Is Todd okay?' Julie asked, fearing the worst.

" 'As far as I know he's fine,' Taylor said between sobs.

" 'Thank goodness! So what's wrong?'

" 'Nothing's wrong,' Taylor said, wiping her eyes.

"Okay, listeners," the radio voice said, "I'm sure you all know that when someone who is crying says nothing is wrong, that always means something is definitely wrong.

"Pursuing the problem Julie said, 'Nothing's wrong? Something must have happened.'

" 'Well, yes there is something,' she said, trying to control her sobs. 'See this?' She held up a sweater. 'I really like this sweater and I take extra good care of it. Look at those spots?' she said, pointing to what looked like catsup stains down the front of it. 'Tara asked me if she could borrow it yesterday and I said okay but to be really careful with it. Look. It's ruined!'

" 'Well, thank goodness it's only a sweater,' Julie said, heaving a sigh of relief.

" 'Only a sweater? You don't get it, do you? This is not just a sweater, it's my favorite sweater! I'm sick of Tara ruining my things.'

And with that she ran into the bathroom and slammed the door, acting pretty much just like the teenager she was only a few short years before.

" 'Well, I told you not to loan your clothes to her,' Julie called after her in exasperation.

"Tara had borrowed other things of Taylor's and it was becoming a problem so Julie had told her several times not to lend her things to Tara and had told Tara not to borrow from her. It seemed to go in one ear and out the other on both heads. And now there was conflict. Julie was too tired for this.

"Have you noticed, listeners, when we're too tired we often lose our ability to deal with problems appropriately. Well, Julie had lost it. Now on with the story.

"Knocking on the bathroom door, Julie said, 'I'm sorry she stained your sweater, Taylor. I've been afraid this would happen. You need to ask her to pay for the cleaning.'

" 'Stop it, Mom! I'm not asking her to pay for anything. It was a trade—she baby sat for me. I'm sick of you butting in. Just leave me alone.'

"Julie was frustrated," the radio voice went on. "After all, she was just trying to help. And that's the rub. She'd been trying to help by telling her daughter-in-law what to do about a lot of other things too and this was the last straw for Taylor. The problem is we think the best way to help is by telling a person what they should do. It doesn't work. Wise men of old knew it first. In Proverbs it says, 'If thou be wise, be wise for thyself.'¹ That's the key folks. We gotta remember that the solution to a problem lies within the person who has the problem. Our job is to just listen and do our best to understand what they're going through."

"Hmmmm," Lindsey said, thoughtfully. "I can relate to Taylor not wanting her mother-in-law to butt in, but how does a person handle something like this?"

"Very simple. Let's listen in."

The radio host continued. "Here's how to handle this kind of situation: first of all she needed to let her daughter-in-law feel what she was feeling, even if she was expressing what she thought was unwarranted anger. That's only a temporary feeling that often goes along with being disappointed or upset about something. It's best to just ignore the comment and it will go away much faster.

"Next, resist telling her what to do. It's amazing what will happen if you just acknowledge her feelings with a comment like, 'That's hard, honey, I know how much you like that sweater.' Then respect her enough to say, 'What are you going to do?' Just watch how smart she'll become. She'll likely say something like, 'I'm not going to loan my clothes to Tara anymore.' Then say, 'Good idea.' And let it be. In some situations you may want to add, 'Is there anything I can do to help?' That's still leaves the responsibility where it belongs."

"Does it really work like that?" Lindsey asked.

"Yes, it really does. I've seen it happen more times than I can count."

"So, that *is* your voice," she said with a knowing smile.

Gigi ignored the comment and said, "Are you getting this, Lindsey?"

"I think so."

"This is one of the most important things you can learn to bring peace into your marriage and your relationship with your future mother-in-law. It's not just a matter of listening; it's a matter of listening with your heart, doing your best to really understand what the other person is going through."

"So, how does it apply in Marianne's situation with her mother-in-law?"

Gigi took her hand and off they went again, back to the family reunion in the canyon. They moved right behind Helen and Marianne so they could hear their conversation.

"I really am worried about these cataracts, Marianne," Helen said.

"That would be a worry, Mom. I've never had cataracts, so I'm not sure how I'd feel. What are you going to do?"

Gigi nudged Lindsey's arm and, with a big grin, said, "Did you hear that? She's got it!"

"Oh, Marianne, I don't know what to do. I'm just scared."

"I think I would be, too," Marianne said, and you could tell she meant it. *"Is there anything I can do to help you?"*

"Bingo!" Gigi almost shouted.

"No. But thank you. I know I've got to have it done, and the doctor assured me everything would be fine." Helen went on, *"It just seems like it's been one thing after another. A few months ago my back went out and I had to go to the chiropractor three times a week to get it back to normal. And before that it was the problem with my teeth."*

"Mom, you really have had a tough year." She took Helen's hand in her own and said, *"I think all that would be very hard."*

"It has been hard, dear." She squeezed Marianne's hand.

For the first time Marianne felt a genuine love for Helen.

"Let's eat!" came the shout from the picnic tables. And the conversation was over.

After the meal, Helen took her son Ryan aside and said, "Ryan, I love your wife so much. She's the only one in this family who really cares about me."

"Oh, my goodness! It does work," said Lindsey. "And it happened in just one conversation. Can it actually work that fast?"

"It's the window of a listening heart. It works magic. Keep it open always and it will lead you to a good relationship with your own mother-in-law . . . and with your husband."

"Maybe so. I'm starting to feel a little better about saying yes to Jeff."

❀❀❀

"I'm going to show you another example of how this works. As you've seen, not all family reunions are a piece a' cake. Some families have so many contentious feelings flying around that there's no way they can get the whole clan together. Take the Jenkins family, for instance. Samuel and Andrea Jenkins are visiting in the home of their son, Sean, and daughter-in-law, Jessica, reviewing the plans for their upcoming reunion."

"We're so excited," Andrea said. "We want everyone to be there, all six of our children and all of our grandchildren. It's going to be so much fun."

"Well, I don't know what to say, Mom," Sean said. "We love being with you and Dad and the rest of the family, except, well, we can't be there if Beverly's going to come."

"I had hoped your differences with your sister had been worked out," she said.

"I'm sorry to say that it's only gotten worse. Jessica can't be with her. It's just too hard on her. I'm never again going to put my wife through that."

"What happened?" Samuel asked his son.

"It goes back to the time we borrowed some money from Beverly for a down-payment on a car for Jessica. We had a deal that it would be paid back in monthly payments, but we hit hard times and Jessica missed two months. We've paid back all but those two payments, but Beverly is still upset at us about it. We'll pay those two as soon as we can."

"I'm interrupting the story right now, Lindsey, to tell you something important," Gigi said. "Don't invite money problems. Money almost always causes trouble in family relationships. Shakespeare was right on the 'money' when in *Hamlet* he said, 'Neither a borrower nor a lender be.'[2] You can help in other ways, but there's something about money that makes people weird. Just a little side lesson there, no charge. Now back to the Jenkins."

"Samuel, maybe we could pay it for them so they can all have good feelings for the reunion," Andrea said to her husband.

"That's not a good idea, Andrea. It would only increase the bad feelings. This is their problem and they need to work it out, and I trust that they will. It may take a little time, but they will."

Andrea, still trying to solve the problem, said, "Sean, maybe you and Jessica could call Beverly and tell her when you think you'll have the money; then she'll feel better about it."

"Mom, we already tried that. Jessica called her and Beverly actually screamed at her and hung up. What's going on with her, anyway?"

"Mom," Jessica said, "I just can't be where Beverly is right now. Please try to understand. I just can't come to the reunion."

"What do you do in a case like this, Gigi? It'll be sad if they're not there," Lindsey said.

"Yes, it will be. But I can guarantee it'll be sadder if they do come. It'll ruin the whole reunion. Samuel's got the picture in focus. Listen."

"Jessica, we do understand. There's no way we would put you in that difficult situation. We love you too much to do that," Samuel said.

Andrea could see he was on target in this and said, "That's right, Jessica. Time will heal this and there will be other reunions." They both hugged their daughter-in-law and son.

"They weren't just listening, they were understanding Jessica's feelings and seeing the problem from her point of view. It made all the difference. Her love for them could not help but grow stronger," Gigi said.

❀❀❀

"Now on we go to help you understand this process of empathy from yet another angle. We're going to drop in cold turkey on Cheryl Miller. She and her husband Pete have three kids and live a couple of hundred miles away from both of their parents. Pete made darn sure of that. He didn't want interfering in-laws dropping in whenever they pleased, and he feels he's done his duty if he visits once or twice a year. Cheryl's talking on the phone to her mother-in-law, Pat."

"I'm so mad at Pete I could scream! I have to talk to someone and I can't call my mother or she'll say something to Pete that will make matters worse. She's already said too much, and believe me, he doesn't appreciate it. Every time I say anything she considers it her duty to preach a sermon to him better than any fired-up preacher I ever saw, so I can't talk to her about anything that's troubling me, if it involves Pete. If I do she goes after him and he takes it out on me." Cheryl was plowing full steam ahead.

"Go ahead, honey," Pat said, *"I understand. Believe me, I know how it feels to be mad at Pete."*

"He is so inconsiderate! He doesn't get it that I need his help since the baby came. It's hard with three kids. If he would just help out more

when he comes home from work. But, no, like last night, he comes in like some kind of stupid teenager, throws his coat on a chair, turns on the TV and just sits there, oblivious to the world. It's not fair! He's got ears, can't he hear the baby crying and the other kids fighting? Can't he see that I'm feeling like a wrung-out dishrag?"

"You're right, that's not fair," said Pat in absolute agreement. "I'll be right there with my frying pan to knock some sense into that son of mine."

"I wish!" said Cheryl, chuckling slightly. "I would stand by and applaud."

"Seriously though, is there anything you would like me to do?" Pat asked.

"No. I don't want him to know I've been griping. I just needed to talk to someone, and I knew you would listen without trying to fix it and make matters worse."

"Cheryl, you know you can call me any time."

"Thanks so much for listening, Mom. I feel better already."

"Well, that ended on a good note," Lindsey said.

"Things usually do when you just listen with your heart, do your best to understand what they're going through, and don't try to tell them what to do. If they want your opinion they can ask for it. Until they do it's a good idea to keep it to yourself."

❀❀❀

"Let's look in on one more example. It's a remarkable one. Mary Beth's twenty-three-year-old son, Seth, was killed in an industrial accident. It was a terrible shock to her and the whole family. Everyone was in the deepest kind of mourning, just trying to make some sense out of this horrific tragedy."

"Oh, Gigi, I can only imagine how horrible such a thing would be. I don't know how a mother could bear it."

"No one knows just how difficult it is unless they've lost a child of their own. Children are not supposed to die first. Two days after the accident Mary Beth's mother-in-law, Debra, was visiting her. Listen to their conversation."

The two women were sitting at the kitchen table looking at photographs of Seth, with tear-filled eyes.

"I can't bear that this happened," Debra sobbed. "I love him so much."

"We all do. I can't . . . I can't believe he's gone," Mary Beth was crying from the depth of her soul. "He's my baby. This can't be happening."

Wiping tears that wouldn't stop, Debra, who had been Seth's adoring grandmother, said, "You may have given him birth, but he was my boy!"

Mary Beth appeared stunned by the statement.

"That's a terrible thing to say to a mother at a time like this," Lindsey said.

"I agree. Now here's the remarkable part, Lindsey. In her mind Mary Beth was screaming 'He's not your son, he's mine ... mine ... mine! No one could feel the loss greater than I'm feeling it. I'm his mother!' But instead of saying it, she put herself in her mother-in-law's shoes and felt the reality of this grandmother's pain. Debra had been very close to Seth. Instead of expressing anger at such a heartless statement, look what Mary Beth did."

They watched as Mary Beth put her arms around her mother-in-law and held her close for several minutes. Both women cried together, giving comfort to each other. For the first time in her life Lindsey understood the power of genuine empathy.

"Even during life's most tragic moments we can still call on our better selves and give the love and understanding that's needed," Gigi said.

"To sum it up, here are my Pertinent Points for this window: open your ears more and your mouth less, and put yourself in the other person's shoes to see how it feels.

"Let's go. We have more windows to open."

Chapter Three
Window of Boundaries

*T*hanks to some TV shows Lindsey had seen, she knew where they were and what was happening. The doctor was moving the ultra sound instrument across the belly of the young woman, about her own age. A young man, obviously the pregnant woman's husband, held her hand. All eyes were focused on the screen where they could see the baby moving inside the mother.

"That's Mary and Robert," Gigi said, "witnessing their tiny little miracle in motion."

"It's a boy!" announced the doctor. "No doubt about it. And he's healthy and strong; his measurements show he's right on target."

"Look at his tiny fists, all clenched up," said the young father. "And his feet; look at those feet! Hooray, he's got two of them! And they're big ones."

"He's going to be a big boy," said the doctor.

"And his little nose, look at that! Oh, Robert, he's so cute!" said the young mother. "Thank you, doctor, thank you!"

"Hey, don't thank me. Thank each other, and the good Lord."

"They look so happy, Gigi," Lindsey said, "but why are we here?"

"Because they are about to encounter an interesting in-law dilemma, one that is often faced by new parents."

"But I'm not even married yet, so what's the rush? You know something I don't know?"

"I know you want to have children."

Next thing Lindsey knew it was nearly five months later and they were in the room Mary and Robert were preparing for the baby. The soon-to-be-parents were hanging a musical Winnie-the-Pooh mobile over the crib. A matching changing table was in one corner and next to it a dresser with Winnie-the-Pooh handles on the drawers and a Winnie-the-Pooh lamp on top. Piglet, Eeyore and Tigger were clinging to the wall above the crib. Everything in the nursery was ready for the new arrival.

Finding it awkward to embrace his wife from the front, Robert moved behind Mary, put his arms around her and softly said, "I love you so much, sweetheart. Just think, we're going to be parents. We'll bring our little son home and just the three of us will be a family together."

"I can hardly wait. Mom's not coming to help until we say, so let's just be us for a few days, okay?"

"I like that idea," he said. *"I'm so glad my boss is giving me a few days off when the baby comes."*

Suddenly strains of Rock-A-Bye-Baby came from the hall. "It's the phone. I'll get it," said Mary.

"Whoa! These people are over the top with this baby thing," Lindsey said.

"Just you wait. You'll be every bit as crazy when baby fever hits you."

"I *am* waiting. I'm going to be married a good long while before I have a baby," she said with unfounded confidence.

"You're funny. Just as soon as that wedding ring starts feeling at home, it'll hit." Gigi predicted. "I know you."

"No, you don't," she laughed.

"Oh, yes, I do," she said with a smile.

"Hello," said Mary.

"Hi, How are you feeling?"

Putting her hand over the receiver Mary said, "It's your mother, Robert." Then back into the phone, "Just fine, in fact, too fine."

"No labor pains yet?"

"None, darn it."

"Can I talk to Robert?"

"Here he is."

"Hi, Mom."

"Dad and I have been thinking. Since this is our first grandchild we would really like to be there for the birth. It's so exciting we don't want to miss anything. And I know Mary will need my help for about a week when she comes home from the hospital, so we're planning on staying on as a support system for you."

"Well, uh, that's . . uh. . very nice. Uh, well . . . great."

"Call us as soon as the labor begins. As you know, it takes a few hours to get there and we don't want to miss the action."

"Okay, g'bye, Mom." He hung up the phone.

"What's the matter? What did your mother say?"

"They're coming for the birth."

"No! This is our special time. Why didn't you tell her? Anyway, my mom is coming to help and I certainly don't need two grandmas fighting over who gets to hold the baby."

"Houston, we have a problem," said Robert in his best astronaut voice, trying to put a light touch on a heavy problem.

"That's for sure. Oh, Robert, what are we going to do so we don't hurt anybody's feelings?"

"Now that *is* a problem, Gigi. What can they do in a situation like this?"

"This is a defining moment for Mary and Robert," Gigi said, "and they're smart enough to want to do it right."

"Can't they just turn on the radio and have you tell them what to do?"

Ignoring her comment, Gigi said, "Like I said, they're smart. They have several friends who have children, so they asked them for suggestions. It's a good idea to talk with a few trusted people who have been through it. Might as well learn from someone else's mistakes and save yourself a ton of misery. After listening to a lot of advice and talking it out together, they came up with a plan. Did you get that, Lindsey?"

"Yeah. They asked others how they did it."

"Right. However, there's another important point. They talked with each other about it so they could come up with what would work for them. Very smart. Here they are, the next day, on the phone, putting their plan into action."

"Hi, Mom. It's Robert . . ."

". . . and Mary" she joined in.

"We've got it on speaker phone so we can both talk. Could you get Dad on the line, too?" Robert said.

"It's Robert!" she shouted excitedly into the room.

"He's on now. Has the labor started?"

Robert began. "Not yet. We're very excited to have you come and we've made a decision about your visit."

"They're following their plan," Gigi said, "which is that Robert will do most of the talking. That's important. They're his parents so he's taking the lead to avoid resentment toward Mary."

"We have a new plan," Robert continued. "My boss has given me a few days off when the baby comes. We've decided that we'd like to be alone with our baby for those few days before either of our parents come. We're looking forward to this special time with just the three of us. We hope you will understand how important this is to us."

"What?" said his mother, incredulously. "But we were counting on coming for the birth."

"I know, Mom, and we're very pleased that you want to be here. I'll be home for three days so I can help with the baby. When I go

back to work Mary's mother will be here for five days and then we were hoping you and Dad could come for the next five days after she leaves. Our baby's going to need some time to get acquainted with his grandparents . . . individually."

"I'm really looking forward to your coming at that time," Mary said. "I'll need the help of parents more when Robert goes back to work. We hope this will work for you. It'll mean a lot to us."

"We understand," said Robert's dad. "I think it's important for you to have some time alone."

"Thanks, Dad, Mom, for being so understanding. I love you both and want you to be an important part of our son's life."

"Yes, we love you and appreciate you very much," Mary added.

"I'll call you as soon as the baby pops into the world." said Robert.

"I call that a job well done," said Gigi.

"Me, too, but I don't think Robert's mother is happy about this new turn of events."

"Nobody said everybody has to be happy all the time. She'll get over it because Robert and Mary were kind, and they continued to be kind, without allowing themselves to be controlled. Keeping the window of understanding open while boundaries are set in place makes it all work.

"New parents have to set boundaries, and the sooner they do it the better off everyone is. Otherwise they're going to end up knee-deep in a whole lot of misery. They just need to do it in a kindly manner, as Mary and Robert did. Appropriate boundaries don't ruin relationships, they become the foundation for healthy ones. Can you imagine the resentment Mary would have felt toward her mother-in-law if they had not set this boundary? It may have festered for years, with her in-laws jumping in on them any time they pleased."

❀❀❀

"I've got a question, Gigi. What if they hadn't set the boundary and things did get worse. Can you set boundaries long after they should have been set? Like years later when the relationship has gotten really bad? For instance, my cousin Caleb and his wife Sophie have been suffering through that misery for the past seven years. He told me all about it at our family reunion last year. His mother-in-law considers it her divine duty to raise her grandchildren. She literally moves in for a few months after the baby is born and takes over. She did it on the first and again on the second, and stayed at least three months! Can you believe it? Their third child was due a few weeks after the reunion and he said his mother-in-law had her bags packed and was ready to move in again. It's driving them crazy. They have always wanted four children, but he said her visits are making them think about not having another baby."

"I call that cruel and unusual birth control," Gigi said. "Have you talked to him since the reunion?"

"No. I haven't seen them for almost a year."

"Then let's go visit them right now."

Gigi took Lindsey by the hand and in no time at all they were there, right in the middle of a discussion that was taking place between her cousin, Caleb, and his wife, Sophie.

Feeling uncomfortable, Lindsey said, "Gigi, this is my cousin. I really don't think I should be eavesdropping on them. I'm going to wait outside."

"No you're not. You're the reason we're here, so don't duck out when the answer to your question is about to be revealed before your very eyes."

"Okay. Okay."

"This conversation they're having," Gigi said, " is taking place one month after their third baby was born. It's bedtime and Lila, the grandmother, is in the nursery rocking the baby to sleep. Caleb and Sophie are down the hall in Caleb's study with the door shut."

"Sophie, I've had it! Every time I pick up Brady your mother moves in on me and practically snatches him right out of my arms. You saw her a few minutes ago when she said, 'Good grief, Caleb, you don't hold a baby like a football! He needs his grandma.' And she took him right out of my arm, where, I might add, he was tucked as safe as if I were running for a touchdown. I felt like snatching him right back, but it didn't seem right to fight over the baby, especially in front of our little girls.

"And that brings up another point," he went on. "Yesterday when Ellie didn't want to eat her beans, and I told her she didn't have to eat them all, just two bites. Well, your lovely mother butts in and says, 'No Caleb, she'll eat them all. Ellie, kids in Africa are starving. Eat your beans, dear, every bite. Grandma knows best.'

"Sophie, she's undermining us, and I want her out of here!" Caleb said and meant it.

"I'm with you, Caleb," Sophie said. "Yesterday when Ellie's little friend Suzy came to play I was telling her Ellie couldn't play yet because she wasn't quite finished cleaning her room. Ellie wasn't happy about that and started to protest. What did my mother do? She butted in and said, 'Of course she can play. I'll finish your room Ellie. Come on in Suzy and you two go play.' Then she turned to me and said, 'Kids are only young once.' I didn't want to make a scene in front of the kids, so I let it go, but I was boiling mad inside. I've had it, too. Oh, Caleb, what are we going to do?"

Caleb stood up and said, resolutely, "We're gonna lay down the law. We're gonna set some boundaries with your mother, and that's going to include sending her home. This is our home, Sophie, and these are our kids, and we're perfectly capable of raising them, and doing things our way!"

"You're absolutely right," Sophie said, nearly as militant as Caleb. Then softening, said, "But she is my mother and I don't want to hurt her. How are we going to do this?"

"Okay, this is going to take a little figuring out," Caleb said, sitting back down. "We need to do it the right way, whatever the right way is."

"Caleb, no matter how we do this my mother's feelings are going to be hurt. Our challenge is doing it in a way that hurts her the least."

"Exactly. Hmmmm. So how do we do that?" Then, as if a light bulb went off in Caleb's head, he said, "Hey, I know. Let's google up some help on setting boundaries."

He went to his computer, and Sophie pulled up a chair beside him. They went from site to site, until they hit upon something that made sense to them.

Caleb began reading from the screen. "It is important to remember that boundaries are set by being kind, gentle, respectful, and firm. You can set any boundary and still keep a good relationship with your parents if you stay in control of yourself and use these guidelines. It's when we lose control and forget to be kind, gentle, and respectful that the relationship becomes strained and broken. On the other hand, when we are only kind, gentle, and respectful without being firm, then the problem can go on endlessly, which also leads to strained and broken relationships between parents and grown children."[3]

"That's it!" Sophie said. "We can do this."

"They made a plan," Gigi said, "They even role played it, then put it into action. They waited until the following evening when the kids were all in bed and things were calm, and they were casually sitting in the living room. Let's look in on them implementing the plan."

Sophie said, "Mom, something's happening and we really need to discuss it now."

"Sounds ominous," her mother said.

"Mom," Sophie said, "While I was growing up you taught me many things, and you really set a good example. And you and Dad both set a good example of parenting. I really miss Dad and I know you do, too." Sophie hesitated, then said, "I'm not sure how to say what I need to say."

"*Just say it right out. That's how you were taught,*" Lila said.

"*Okay. I'll do it.*" Clearing her throat she went on. "*Caleb and I have been married for ten years and little Brady is our third child. You've been here a month and we've appreciated your help; however, now it's gone beyond help to where it seems like . . . well, our lives are being run by you. We need to be able to live in our home our way, and care for our children our way. So far our other two kids seem to be doing just fine.*"

Lila chimed in, "*Yes, they are. Thanks to me for coming and helping them get the best start possible.*"

"*Much of your help has really been appreciated,*" Sophie said. "*Yet some of the help has not . . . Oh, Mom, I'm not sure how to say this. The first two weeks were a great help, but beyond that Caleb and I needed to take over and get on with being the parents.*"

Lila was about ready to say something, but before she had a chance Sophie went on. "*Now, Mom, you can take this one of two ways. You can get hurt, get angry, go home and withdraw and deprive our children of their grandmother. Or you can begin to understand our need to have our home be our home, not yours. I need to be the one rocking my baby to sleep, Caleb needs to be holding his son, the way daddies hold sons. You know he loves him and would never hurt him. In other words, Mom, it's time we returned to normal life. And it's time for you to return to your life and your home.*"

"*I get it. You're kicking me out,*" her mother said.

Caleb jumped in and said, "*You know, Mom, you could look at it that way, but all we're doing is asking you to understand that we need to just be our little family here alone now.*"

"*I was only trying to help,*" she said, dabbing her eyes with a tissue. "*But I can see I'm not welcome here any more.*"

"Mom," Sophie said, "you will always be welcome to visit our home, but it will need to be on our terms."

"That's right, Mom," Caleb said. "You'll always be welcome here, but not for extended lengths of time."

"So, you're not only kicking me out, but you're limiting the length of my visits," she said, sitting up abruptly. "Fine, I'll go pack my bags right now. I know when I'm not wanted."

"Did you hear us, Mom? You're always welcome and wanted," Sophie said. "Life in every family has to return to normal, and that time has come in our family."

Caleb said, "We hope, as you think about this, you will understand our needs, and also our love for you."

Sophie put her arm around her mother and said, "We love you, Mom. We just need our family back."

Sniffing, Lila said, "I was just trying to help."

"We know and we appreciate it," Caleb said.

Sophie said, "Now how can I help you make arrangements for your return flight?"

"I'm perfectly capable of taking care of it myself," she said as she got up to leave the room.

"Let us know if there is anything we can do to help," Caleb said.

After she left the room Sophie sat down by Caleb and said, "Oh, that was so hard to do because I really do love my mother."

He said, "I know, and I appreciate your courage to do what needed to be done."

"Oh, wow!" said Lindsey. "What a hard thing to have to do. I hope I could be that strong if I needed to be."

"You could," Gigi said. "I know you."

"But all I can picture is Sophie's mother sitting in her room crying and feeling unloved."

"That's exactly what she did. She had to go through that part, but don't sell this good woman short. Let's look in on her and the family the next morning."

Sohpie and Caleb were in their room finishing dressing when they heard a light knock on the door.

"May I come in?" said Lila.

Caleb opened the door and said, "Of course, come on in." He motioned for her to sit in the chair and they sat on the edge of the bed.

Lila spoke softly, "Sophie, you were right, that I could take this one of two ways, and when I went to my room last night I felt hurt and unloved, thinking that I would go home and withdraw. But that isn't the way I raised you and that isn't the way I need to behave. I laid there in bed and I thought about when I was a young mother, and how much I would have resented someone coming into my home and taking over, and I knew what I needed to do. I had forgotten how it was to be a young mother with a young family. Forgive me, dear. I so want to be a good mother and grandmother because I love you, and Caleb I love you, too, and I love your precious children."

She went on, "Later this morning when I make my flight arrangements I want to make sure what schedule will work for you."

"Talk about a group hug," Gigi said. "Well, that was the best one ever. And here's another good part about this whole scenario. Lila returned home, buried herself in volunteer work, and even joined a quilting club. And I'm betting some little grandkids are going to be getting some mighty cute quilts in the near future."

"So she got a life of her own, it sounds like," Lindsey said.

"Yes, and she's happier than she's been for years. Besides that, she has the best relationship she's ever had with her daughter and her family. All because two young parents were kind, gentle, respectful, and firm in setting their boundaries.

"So you see, Lindsey, it's never too late to set a boundary. It's always easier if it's set right up front before habits and expectations are stuck in their grooves, but it's never too late."

"I'm glad for my cousin that this all worked out so well after all," Lindsey said.

"Me too. Now I'm going to show you how this boundary setting thing worked in another case," Gigi said. "Let's look in on Jerry and his wife Keira to see how this couple handled their mother-in-law intrusions, which were different but the same principles apply. Hold on, Lindsey."

❀❀❀

Next thing Lindsey knew they were in a home with a couple, probably in their thirties. The living room was furnished in a contemporary style, with a couple of toy trucks and a teddy bear on the floor still waiting to be put away. The clock on the wall ticked to ten o'clock.

"Finally the kids are asleep and we have some time to ourselves," Jerry said to his wife as she plopped down on the sofa. *"I brought you a surprise."*

"You did?" she said with a smile. *"What is it?"*

He sat beside her. *"Something you've been wanting."* He handed her a CD.

"Oh, Jerry! And it isn't even my birthday or anything," she said throwing her arms around him. *"I have been wanting this CD for a long time."*

"I know."

"Thank you so much. Let's listen to it right now. The songs are so romantic."

"I know," he said again, this time with a glint in his eye.

They sat on the sofa listening. After the first song he moved closer and put his arm around her. By the third song she was sitting on his lap. Then he unbuttoned the top button on her shirt. She helped him unbutton the second one.

"Gigi, I think we better leave now," Lindsey said feeling a little embarrassed.

"No need," she said. Just then the phone rang.

"Well, we know who that is!" Jerry said as he got up to answer the phone.

"Hello, Mom. Yes, we're fine. And you? Oh, I'm sorry that happened. Are you okay? Good. I'm glad it was nothing serious. Hey, Mom, can this wait? I'm kinda busy right now."

"Oh, Gigi," Lindsey said, "this could so easily be Jeff and me if I married him."

"The perfect reason for us to be here," Gigi said. "Let's watch and see what happens."

Jerry's mother didn't take the hint and the conversation went on for the next twenty minutes. After the first five minutes, Keira got up and turned off the CD and buttoned her blouse.

"Jerry," Keira said after he hung up, "when are you going to tell your mother to stop calling us every night of our lives? Next time let's just not answer."

"But I'm afraid it might be something serious, Keira."

"Believe me, it's getting to be something serious," she said.

"You're right," he said. "Every night is ridiculous!"

"She called every night?" Lindsey said, finding that hard to believe.

"Every night, and always about bedtime," Gigi said, "thinking only of herself, not about them and their need for time without her intrusions. It didn't seem to matter that he had already called her that morning. It was almost as if she still had to tuck her little boy into bed at the end of the day.

"Lindsey, this is an important thing for you to understand. The marriage needs to be a priority for both husband and wife in order for the greater family happiness to be realized.

Continually putting your marriage relationship on hold—always letting other family members come first—can create a serious problem."[4]

"So what happened? Did Jerry do anything about it?"

"He did, after talking it over with Keira and their deciding on a plan that worked for them. And he was pretty creative about how he did it. He went to his mother's house shortly after that and had a conversation with her about it. Watch."

Handing his mother a small bouquet of flowers he kissed her on the cheek and said, "How are you today, Mom?"

"Really fine, now that you're here, son."

They visited for a few minutes, then he took a deep breath in preparation for setting the boundary. This was not easy for him, but he knew he had to do it for the good of his marriage.

"Mom, Keira and I love you very much, and we have a favor to ask of you."

"I'm happy to do anything you need," she said. "What can I do for you?"

"Oh, this is going to hurt," Lindsey said. Gigi nodded with that all-knowing smile.

"Mom, Keira and I don't have much time alone together and sometimes your phone calls come at a time that's a bit of a problem for us. We were wondering if maybe you could call Keira a couple of times a week during the daytime to chat with her about the kids and such—she'd enjoy that—and then maybe a couple of times a week call me in the early evening. Tuesdays and Saturdays are good times for me.

That way I can find out what's going on with you without taking away from the limited time I have with my family. We'll still be calling you like we already do. Of course, if there's an emergency you can call us any time."

"Oh, I'm so sorry. I just want to check on you at the end of the day. I didn't intend to intrude," she said, obviously hurt.

"I know you didn't, Mom. I hope you can understand. Will this new plan work for you? We love you and we want to hear from you."

"Please forgive me, son. I guess I just didn't think. I'll be happy to do as you have requested."

"It was that simple?" Lindsey asked. "Did it work?"

"Yes, it did. And they treated her with love and respect whenever she called them or they called her. Most mothers want their children to be happy and may not realize that what they're doing is detracting from that. If this boundary had not worked, Jerry and Keira were prepared to get caller ID and be selective about the calls they took from her. Fortunately, they didn't have to do that."

❀❀❀

"Now I'm going to open this boundaries window a little wider," Gigi said, "and you just might find it a bit uncomfortable along the way."

Lindsey's curiosity was piqued. And before she knew it they were on their way to a different home. The names Ken and Jill Foster were on the mailbox. It was a comfortable home, not too large, not too small. Obviously they had lived there for some time, it looked settled into. As usual, they entered the home of these strangers without the slightest qualm. On the family room wall was a plaque with tiny blue violets decorating the words "Our Gifts from Heaven." Under it hung the photos of small children.

"Their grandchildren," Gigi said.

"That would be my guess," Lindsey said.

"I'm not guessing. The baby, Kerilyn, is just three months old, the first child of their youngest son Lynn and his wife Keri—the focus of our attention."

"She's adorable," Lindsey said. "So much hair for such a young baby."

"She came with it," Gigi said.

"Like I didn't know," Lindsey whispered under her breath.

The clock showed 8:15 P.M. Jill was sitting on the country-blue sofa and Ken was in his matching recliner. They were eating hot fudge sundaes.

"I'm exhausted, Ken, and so frustrated." She set the bowl down as if she were too tired to finish it. "I'm not up to this again. Taking care of Kerilyn every day is not what I had in mind for this time of my life. Don't get me wrong, I love this grandbaby dearly, but I've already paid my dues. Twice. I raised our four kids and then took care of David and Carrie's baby for a year; now I have other things to do. In fact, I've really looked forward to this time when I could do those other things."

Ken was listening as he finished his ice cream.

"It's not that I didn't enjoy raising our kids. I did, but now it's my time. Except it's not my time. When I became president of the Women's

Aid Society a year ago I knew it would be a rewarding opportunity to serve, and I'm really enjoying it. But it's so difficult to go places and meet with people when I have to take the baby along. It takes me half the time just getting her bundled up and into her carrier seat and then strapped back into the car seat at every stop. Now I know why babies are born to young people. I'm too old for this. And when she starts crying and needs my attention—and it doesn't matter where I am—I get so frustrated. I end up changing my plans and just heading for home. It's wearing me out."

"Well," said Ken, "I'm not excited about it either. Before you started baby-sitting Kerilyn full-time I used to be able to call you and say 'meet me for lunch' and the two of us could be together . . . alone. I miss being able to do that."

"So do I. I wouldn't mind baby-sitting her on occasion, but not like this. I'm beginning to resent Lynn and Keri and I don't like that feeling, Ken."

He jumped in with both feet. "They brought this baby into the world, and we're happy they did, but she's their baby, not ours. She needs her own parents taking care of her. They want us to sacrifice, but they're not willing to."

"Problem is," Jill said, "I'm afraid we set a precedent when we took care of David's baby a couple of years ago, and now we're stuck."

"Precedent be hanged! We're not stuck. Life changes," Ken said.

"Why is Jill taking care of their baby, anyway?" Lindsey asked Gigi.

"Because Keri has a job she really enjoys and she doesn't want to give it up. She and Lynn claim they need her paycheck to make ends meet, which is true only because they've confused putting food on the table with driving the latest SUV. They've pretty much got their needs and wants mixed up."

"It seems to me like they're not looking at his parents' needs and wants at all. Why don't they get a baby-sitter, or take her to a nursery?"

"Because Keri said she wants someone who really loves Kerilyn to take care of her, and that would only be a family member, which is admirable," Gigi said.

"So why don't they just cut back so *she* can stay home with her baby? I think she's being selfish." Lindsey felt the wisdom coming forth from her very own lips and liked the feel of it.

"You seem to know the answer, but unless you're careful, you may find yourself in this same type of situation," Gigi warned.

"I wouldn't do that to my parents."

"Okay, let's find out. First of all, let's see if you understand the process of growing up. If you do, then you'll avoid falling into this trap *and* you'll save your parents and in-laws from falling in as well," Gigi said.

"The growing-up process? I'm an adult with a responsible job, definitely already grown up. So I don't think you're talking about me."

"Oh, yes, I am," she said, "As long as parents make life easy for their children by taking on their burdens, the children remain children. Let's get personal. Where do you live right now?"

"At home," she answered.

"At your *parents'* home. Not *your* home. You're twenty-four years old. Why aren't you living in an apartment of your own? Don't answer that. I already know. Because it's cheaper living at home. Cheaper for whom? You, not them. Who buys most of the groceries? Not you."

"But I eat out most of the time."

"Not all of the time. Who pays the electric bill, the heat bill? Not you."

"Hey, I offered to help pay and they said no."

"And you fell right into the trap of remaining a child. Convenient isn't it? But not fair for your parents or you." Gigi was on a roll. "Do they worry and question you when you come home late? Do they fret if they don't know where you are? Do they nag if you eat too much junk food?"

"Yes, and I don't like it. They make me feel like a teenager."

"You're starting to get the picture."

"Gigi, you are hitting below the belt on this one."

"Hurts a little, doesn't it? Hurting's not bad if it helps you grow up a bit more. We'd better hush. Jill is about to say something significant to Ken."

"I was talking about my problem to Charlene the other day—she helps out at the Aid Society sometimes, but she's a full-time social worker. She said we may need to set some boundaries with Lynn and Keri. She suggested we give them a date when they need to have another baby-sitter. She told me to make it clear that we love the baby and them very much, and that we have confidence in their ability to take their own responsibility in caring for their child. She suggested we figure out what

works for us and then follow through. And she warned that we don't get caught up in justifying and explaining our decision. That will avoid any arguing."

"Sounds like wise counsel." He put his empty bowl down and started to get up. "Let's go visit them right now."

"I'll call and make sure it's a good time to come," Jill said, perking up at the thought of a solution.

On the drive over they devised their exact strategy. Gigi and Lindsey followed them into Lynn and Keri's home. The baby was asleep. They all sat down in the living room, did a minute or two of small talk about the baby, then Jill began.

"We have something important to tell you. I can't take care of Kerilyn full-time any longer. I'm happy to help every Thursday, but that's all, with a few rare emergency exceptions."

Lynn and Keri looked at each other in surprise, then dismay.

"But we need you," Keri said.

"That's right, Mom," Lynn said. "We need you. You did it for David, but you won't do it for me?"

"Oh, kids are so clever," said Gigi. "They know how to insert the dagger and then twist it just at the right moment. Goes back to my theory that a child's main job is to get his or her needs met at all cost. And it doesn't matter the age. Indeed, they are crafty little beggars. And they'll do it until they're forced to grow up."

Lynn took another stab at it. "I don't know what we'll do without your help," he whined.

Jill didn't take the bait. She and Ken were apparently prepared for all sorts of begging. "If you guys weren't so smart and resourceful, I'd be worried," she said. "Dad and I know you'll figure out the best way for you and your baby. Two months from now, March 3rd will be my last day. Don't forget that I can help on Thursdays after that, if it's needed," said Jill.

"Well, we've got to go. We love you guys," Ken said.

They hugged and then left.

"So what happened?" Lindsey asked.

"Oh, Lynn and Keri were not happy about this at all."

"Kind of like you said, Gigi, everybody doesn't have to be happy all the time."

"That's right. That's not real life. It's the unhappy, tough times that help us find out what we're made of. It wasn't easy for Lynn and Keri, and it took a lot of soul-searching and planning on their part. They didn't want to leave their baby with anyone else, so they did some serious surgery on their lifestyle. Keri told her boss she could only work part-time and would need to do most of it from home so she could be with her baby. He liked her work, but needed full-time help for her particular job, so he offered her a lesser job in his company at lower pay that could be done at home. To her credit, she took it."

Gigi went on, "Do they have everything they want? No. Are they happier? Yes. She's loving this time with her baby.

And Jill and Ken are a lot happier, too. Interestingly, their relationship with Lynn and Keri has improved significantly. All because boundaries were set in a kind and respectful way."

❀❀❀

"So," Lindsey said, "You think I should get an apartment, huh?"

"What do *you* think would be best for you? While you're figuring that out, we've got a couple of stops to make before opening any more new windows."

"Where are we going?"

Suddenly they were standing in the middle of . . .

"A chicken coop!" Lindsey said in disbelief. " What are we doing in a chicken coop?"

"We're going to learn a lesson from nature. See that hen over there? She's sitting on an egg, and has been patiently fulfilling that duty off and on for twenty-one days."

The hen waddled away and they watched the egg. It began to crack slightly, all on it's own.

"A baby chick is inside and wants to come out," Lindsey said.

"Brilliant. Keep watching."

Soon they saw a tiny beak make its way out by pecking at the shell from the inside. For a long time they watched that baby chick peck away at the shell. The mother hen made no move to help. It squirmed and wriggled and pecked for most of the day. Obviously, it was a real struggle for the baby chick.

"If nature's so smart, why wasn't the hen designed to help the chick get out? A few good pecks from the mother and the job would be done," Lindsey said.

"True, but what would happen to the baby chick?"

"It would probably really appreciate it, so it could get on with its life."

"Wrong. It would be too weak to survive. You see, it gains its strength from the struggle."

"Okay, okay. I get it. So you don't think I'm struggling enough."

"Let me just say you'll learn a whole lot faster and be much better prepared for the rest of what's ahead if you get out on your own. This is an important thing for parents to learn, too. Ever heard about the eagles?" Gigi said.

Next thing Lindsey knew, they were on top of a high mountain.

"This is breathtaking, so beautiful up here," Lindsey said.

"This is where the eagles live."

Just then one went flying by with a wing span so wide Lindsey ducked out of fear of being attacked.

"No need to worry. You're safe. They don't even know you're here," said Gigi.

The eagle landed gently on its huge nest in the branches of a rather barren tree. The nest must have been at least five feet wide. Two baby eagles greeted their parent with open mouths. The large eagle dropped shredded bits of meat for them to eat.

"Now *there's* a devoted parent," Lindsey said.

"Yes, both parents take very good care of the eggs and then the babies. They are both devoted, and not only to their young. Eagles find a mate and stay true to that mate until their dying day."

"You're right, we can learn a lot from nature."

"Indeed we can," Gigi said. "Look at the bottom of the nest and tell me what you see."

"I see leaves and all kinds of stuff that makes a soft bed for the little eagles."

"Eaglets," Gigi corrected her.

"I knew that."

"And," Gigi said, "it's very comfortable for them. What you don't see is that under the soft bed are sharp sticks pointing up in all directions. When the eaglets are small they can't feel the sharp sticks, but as they grow their weight pushes down on the soft bed and they begin to feel the points of the sticks."

"That could hurt," Lindsey said.

"That's the point . . . no pun intended," she said with a wry smile that regularly accompanied the twinkle in her eyes. "The bigger they get the more uncomfortable the nest becomes. Soon they fly out and make their own life happen."

"Aha," Lindsey said. "Now I get the point . . . and that pun *is* intended. You think my parents should make it more uncomfortable for me to remain at home."

"Lesson learned. A little independence will make for a happier relationship between your husband and your parents. When it comes to boundaries there are so many different applications, and we can't go through them all or we'd be working at it 'til you were an old woman and Jeff was happily, well, maybe not happily, married to someone else. Still, there's one more visit in this window that we need to make. I think it'll serve you well in your particular situation." Off they went.

❀❀❀

The countryside was ablaze with color. It had to be somewhere in the New England states. There was a nip in the air as they followed two young children and their parents, who were loaded with suitcases, up the steps to the door of a lovely colonial-style home. The man gave a knock on the door and then walked in, and so did Gigi with Lindsey at her heels.

"Hi, Mother! We're here."

They were immediately greeted by a well-dressed woman. "Mark! Oh, how good to have you back home again!" She hugged him as if she hadn't seen him for years. "Nice to see you, Trudy," she said rather coolly to the young mother.

Turning her attention to the children she scooped them both up in her arms, almost falling over in her enthusiasm.

"Hi, Grandmama!" they shouted.

"The children are excited," Lindsey said.

"And why wouldn't they be. Every time they come she showers them with new toys. She adores these children. After all, Mark is her only child and they're his children," said Gigi.

"Hmmm. That has a familiar ring to it. You've got me hooked."

"They were here visiting about four months ago. They moved to Virginia and this is their third visit since the move. Trudy's parents live in a nearby town. They both grew up in this area and enjoy coming back to visit. They stay here because Mark's mother has much more room, and she's alone. Only problem is . . . well, I'll let you see. It's the following afternoon and they're about to leave to visit Trudy's parents."

"Get your jackets on, kids. It's time to go," Mark announced.

"Yea! We get to see Grandma and Grandpa Johnson!" Four year-old Annie was jumping up and down. "Will our cousins be there, too?"

"Most of them," Trudy answered, then turned to her mother-in-law. "We'll be back about eleven tonight."

"Now watch this, Lindsey. It's what I call the Great Mother-in-law Manipulation Game."

"We'll be back in no time, Mother," said Mark.
"That's fine, dear. Have a nice time."

"Why don't you come with us? The Johnsons said you're welcome."

"No, I told you I'd rather not intrude."

"Julia, you're welcome to come, really," said Trudy.

"No. I'll be fine here."

"Okay. Well, we'll see you later tonight," said Mark.

About the time they reached the door Lindsey heard a gasp for air, then a cough. It was Julia.

"Oh, my goodness, Gigi. She's got a bad case of asthma."

"Mother, are you okay?" Mark looked scared as he hurried to his mother's side. "It's your asthma, isn't it?"

"I'll be okay. You go and have a good time." Mark turned to go and suddenly she made an even more terrible gasp for air.

Mark dashed to her side again. "Trudy, you and the kids go on. I can't leave Mother."

"Let me help, Mark. Maybe if we get her settled she'll be okay. I'll call my parents and tell them to go ahead without us, that we'll be over later." Turning to the kids she said, "Go play with your toys while we help Grandmama."

"Gigi, this isn't manipulation. This is serious," Lindsey said, feeling very concerned for Julia.

"To speed things along I'm going to tell you what happened. She got worse, and they ended up taking her to the emergency room, with the kids in tow. This was a full-blown attack. She was there a few hours before she felt well enough to go home. By then they missed the family gathering at Trudy's house."

"See, it *was* serious," Lindsey said.

"Oddly, this happened every time they came for a visit. And always just as they were about to leave for the Johnsons'. I wasn't born with blinders on . . . I could see right through it."

"You mean someone can actually schedule an asthma attack?"

"Only if you're really good at it. Sometimes the mind can control the body, you know."

"That's disgusting."

"She did *not* want to share her son or his children with anyone. After a few more visits like this Mark and Trudy figured it out. Then they made a plan. Mark called his mother one day and told her they wouldn't be coming to visit at her house anymore because it was obviously too stressful for her, causing her asthma to act up. He said they would love to have her come and visit them at their home in Virginia instead. Julia balked, but they stuck to it. They still visited Trudy's parents for reunions, but mostly had them come and visit them at their home, also. It worked. Interestingly, Julia never had an attack at their house. After a time, they tried visiting Julia at her home again, and to their amazement, there were no more attacks."

"So, when Mark and Trudy set the boundary the problem was solved. I'm going to remember this." Lindsey was beginning to see that even though problems with Jeff's mother may lie ahead, there were solutions.

"My Pertinent Point here is: setting boundaries kindly can help build a solid foundation for a healthy relationship.

"Let's go open another window," Gigi said. Lindsey took her hand, eager to learn more.

Chapter Four
Window of Forgiveness

They were standing inside a kitchen where an attractive woman—I'm guessing about forty-years old, dark hair—sat at the table writing a letter.

"Do I know her?" Lindsey asked.

"No. Her name is Meredith, and she has two daughters and one son. I want you to see this because what she's about to go through will increase your understanding and help you through future challenges that, though different, may be quite difficult."

"Who's she writing to?"

"Her son, Matthew. He's been divorced twice, the last time only four months ago; and already he's talking about marrying a woman he met just a few weeks ago."

"Gigi, you don't think Jeff and I will end up like this, do you? Is this a warning?" she said, not happy at all with this situation. "I don't like this window."

"Stop worrying. This isn't about you. It's simply a truth I want you to discover. Meredith is very concerned about her son. Read her letter out loud." Gigi said.

"Should we be doing this? Don't you think this is an invasion of privacy?"

"No, because it happened many years ago and much can be learned from it. Read."

"Okay, if you say so." She cleared her throat and began.

"Dear Matt, I've been thinking about our conversation the other day. You said you were thinking of marrying Sharon. This worries me, son. I love you very much and I don't want you to make another mistake. I'll never forget the day you told me your first wife had left you. You stood at our front window and cried like a baby. There was no way I could comfort you. We all thought your marriage would work, but when she found someone else, well, no words can say how my heart ached for you. Then you found Elizabeth. She wasn't at all what you expected and that ended almost before it began, leaving you broken-hearted again.

"Matt, I can't bear the thought of you going through anything like that again. I love you too much for that. So all I'm asking is that you take it slow with Sharon. Please don't rush into anything. You can't possibly know the kind of person she is until you've known her much longer. She may be just fine, and it may all work out, but please take your time. I can't bear to think of you suffering a broken heart again.

"Please know this letter is written with the greatest sense of caring. I just want what is best for you, son. With love, Mother."

"I can understand her concern, Gigi. She doesn't want him hurt again."

"The letter is not the problem. It's what Matt did with the letter that's the problem."

"How's that?"

"He read it to Sharon!" she said with a definite note of disgust.

"You're kidding!"

"And Sharon was incensed. She and Matt got married soon after that and have stayed together for eighteen years and have two beautiful children. However, she has never forgiven her mother-in-law for that letter. It has created a terrible wedge between them."

"That seems so silly. Surely she can see that Matt's mother was just trying to give him a little motherly advice."

"Oh, Lindsey, if only people could see things as they really are. Some just hang on to an ill feeling through the years like a drunk clutching his whiskey bottle. And look at the sorrow it causes."

In a flash, they were in a bedroom where a gray-haired woman was lying on the bed, sobbing softly. Judging from her hands and the lines in her face, she was probably about seventy-something. Just then her husband walked into the room and came over to her. She turned to him.

"That's Meredith!" Lindsey said.

"Grown older, and still pretty as a picture," Gigi said.

"Meredith, what's the matter?" her husband asked, as he sat on the edge of the bed, tenderly taking her hand in his.

"I don't know what to do, Phil," she sobbed out the words. "I've tried so hard to win Sharon over . . . for years. I just called her to invite them over for dinner again and she was rude, like always, and said they wouldn't be coming. She still holds a grudge, even though I've apologized several times for writing that letter. Years ago she said she'd never forgive me for it, and she's holding to it. I told her it was nothing against her. I've even told her that I think she's been a good wife for Matt, but she won't listen. She just says, 'I know what you think of me and I'll never forgive you.' I don't know what to do."

"I know what I want to do," Phil said. "I want to go over there and give her a nice little punch in the nose and wake her up."

"Gigi, I think he's related to you," Lindsey said. She looked out of the corner of her eye at Gigi and saw that wry smile again.

"Well, not really," Phil said. "I'm just sad that she has the power to make you this miserable for such a long time." He put his arms around Meredith and held her close, to comfort her.

"At least she has a loving husband," Lindsey said.

"Thank goodness for that. He's talked to Sharon, too, but just keeps coming up with an empty bucket."

"Meredith seems like such a nice person, why would anyone treat her like that? Why won't Sharon forgive and forget? It's such an unimportant thing to carry a grudge about for so long."

"I'll show you the reason," said Gigi. "Take my hand."

They were in the backyard of a large Tudor home in a wooded area. Other homes were not far away, each on about an acre or more of land, making the homes quite private. Just as they arrived a father and a girl about ten years old came out the back door. She was dressed in a school uniform, a white shirt with a navy skirt. The father had a firm grip on the girl's arm and was yelling at her. The girl looked scared, and was crying.

"Stop bawling!" he yelled. "Don't you ever come home with a report card like that again. An F in math! We don't fail in this family! Do you understand that? We're the Stramfords and we have a reputation to keep. How many times do I have to tell you? Well, you're going to remember it this time." He dragged her over to a tree, pulled off a small branch and began whipping her legs.

She screamed, "Stop, Daddy, stop! I'll do better. I promise!"

He was out of control and kept whipping her. Lindsey couldn't stand to look. "Stop him, Gigi, stop him!" she begged, knowing full well she couldn't.

Finally he stopped, then held her firmly by the shoulders, looked into her face and said, "You'd better, young lady! And do something with that stringy hair. You embarrass me."

With that he abruptly let her go and quickly went back into the house. The little girl fell to the ground crying.

"Oh, Gigi. That poor little girl. I can't stand what he did to her. How can anyone do that to a child?"

"He's a cruel man with his own story to tell, but we're not going there," she said.

"Is this little girl Sharon?"

"Yes," Gigi said. "Meredith's daughter-in-law Sharon. And ever since that day, she has felt inadequate, certain that she never measures up. When children experience abuse from a parent it leaves them responding to an inaccurate perception of the thoughts and feelings of others.[5] In Sharon's case when anything happens that may indicate she is less than what's expected, she becomes that little ten-year-old girl again and recoils to protect herself."

"You mean when she read that letter, she saw Meredith as a symbol of her father?"

"Exactly. The letter to her was like a whipping on her legs," Gigi said.

"But Meredith didn't even really know her yet."

"Doesn't matter. The past becomes the owner of the spirit, until it's put in its place," she said.

"So what can put it in its place?"

"There are a couple of ways to do it, Lindsey. You can look it straight in the face, acknowledge it and say, 'This happened to me and it was terrible.' And then say, 'So what! I'm through letting it control me. So now what?' And then move on with your life as though it didn't happen. If the pain returns, acknowledge the horribleness of it and again say, 'It happened. So what! Now what?' and go on without letting it own you."

"That sounds simple enough," Lindsey said.

"Yes, but it isn't always that simple for some folks. Sometimes they need professional help, particularly if the experience was terribly damaging to their spirit. The past can be conquered. Let me show you another way."

The framed certificates on the wall showed the credentials of Lewis W. Calhoon, Ph.D., a marriage and family therapist. The room was simple but nicely decorated—a mahogany desk at one end, a leather sofa with matching chair at the other. A table lamp was on, shedding light on whatever problem might fill the room. The doctor sat in a modestly upholstered office chair with wheels, facing an ashen-faced woman on the sofa.

"Who is she, Gigi?"

"That's not important. What the doctor is doing to help her, that's what's important. She was molested as a child, over and over, and just finished sobbing her tragic story out to him. The perpetrator was an older man, a neighbor. Someone she trusted. It has ruined her life, and she's come for help."

"How old were you when it first happened?" the doctor asked.

"Five," the woman said, reaching for another tissue.

"And how often did it happen?"

"Once a week for almost two years . . . on the day they tended me while my mother went to her bridge club," she said softly, wiping her tears. "And I couldn't tell anyone. He said it was our secret, and if you tell a secret it makes you a bad person. I was just a little girl and I believed him. And he gave me candy because I was such a good girl for

keeping the secret. And he said if I did tell, no one would believe me anyway and they would call me a liar. It would be terrible to be called a liar. I was so glad when he died."

"So all these years you've told no one?"

"No one. You are the first to know that I was molested, and I feel like garbage."

"You may be surprised at what I'm about to say, but it's true," Dr. Calhoon said. *"You were not molested."*

"You don't believe me! You think I'm lying! He was right." She *started to get up and leave.*

"Wait. I do believe you. But I mean it, you *were not molested; a little five year old girl that used to be* you *was the victim. She's your hero. She survived. You can honor her for what she's gone through, and experience a freedom you've never known before. Are you ready?"*

"But it was *me," she said cautiously, as she sat back onto the sofa.*

"When you were five. But it's not you now. Are you ready for the freedom?"

"Okay, I'm ready," she said, taking a deep breath.

"Here's what you can do, if you choose to," said the doctor. "I call it the Five-Step Program. Follow it exactly and you'll find relief and the beginning of a new life. Here it is:

"Step One: Find the little girl and picture her in your mind.

Step Two: Listen to the little girl. Let her tell you her story.

Step Three: Believe the little girl.

Step Four: Cry for the little girl.

Step Five: Allow the little girl to remain in her own time. She's the hero, not you. You're the product of the hero, and now you're going to honor her by the way you live your life."[6]

He handed her a 3x5 card with the steps listed on it. She silently read through the steps, held the card to her heart for a few seconds, then put it in her purse. Her tears were gone and the color returned to her face.

"Did she do the steps?" Lindsey was fascinated.

"Yes, she did," said Gigi. "And Dr. Calhoon helped her through the process. She's a completely different woman now, enjoying life and the people in that life as never before."

"But what about Sharon? It's too bad she doesn't have a Dr. Calhoon," said Lindsey. "I wish someone could give her a card with the five steps on it. She's still suffering from her anger." "Yes, she is. But there's something about Sharon that eventually opened her eyes. Though she hasn't yet taken her responsibility in this problem with her mother-in-law, she's basically a good woman of faith. And it's her faith that's going to be the window opener for her."

"What do you mean, Gigi? It seems like it would be *Meredith's* faith that would cause a change. She's the humble one."

"Actually, that's very perceptive. Meredith's faith definitely played a role. Look."

We were back in Meredith's bedroom. She was alone kneeling at her bedside praying.

"Dear Heavenly Father, you've heard this prayer before, but I'm asking it again. I'm so sad about the trouble we're having with Sharon. We need her and Matt to be an active part of our family. We want to enjoy their children and give them the kind of love that only

grandparents can give. We want the warmth and joy of our family to fill our home. Please awaken Sharon and help her have a forgiving heart. Help me have a forgiving heart, too, and to love her with the love that you have for her. Thank you for all the blessings you have given to me and my dear Phil. In Jesus' name. Amen."

Lindsey was impressed by the tender pleading of her prayer. It was plain to see there was no animosity or anger in it at all.

"Sometimes prayers take a while getting answered," Gigi said. "Meredith had been praying for Sharon for a long time. And she kept on praying. Sometimes we may think God's sleeping in, when, truth be told, he's been up all night making plans. All things have to happen in their time. Here's one of my favorite scripture verses." She reached in her pocket and pulled out a small laminated card, handed it to Lindsey and said, "Read it."

She obeyed. "To everything there is a season, and a time to every purpose. Ecclesiastes 3:1."

"Perfect," she said. "Now it's yours. Put it in your pocket. You may need it sometime."

Finished with her preaching she continued the story. "Almost a year later Sharon was given a gift from a friend she knew at church. It was a small book titled *Meek and Lowly*. In the first few pages she read something that struck her like a lightning bolt."

"What'd it say?"

"Well, I just happen to have a copy of the book right here, Lindsey." With that Gigi pulled it out of a tapestry purse that seemed to suddenly be hanging on her arm. She wanted to ask her where the purse had come from, but by now nothing surprised her.

"It's right here on page seven," she said, and then began to read. " 'Those who are not meek . . .' do you know what it means to be meek, Lindsey? And don't you dare say shy or weak."

She wasn't sure what she was after, so she made a guess. "Submissive?"

"Yes, to God's will, but not indiscriminately to everybody else's. Too many people get that part mixed up. And it means to be humble, teachable and willing to learn. Wonderful qualities to have. Let's see, where was I? Oh, yes.

> " 'Those who are not meek are often reluctant to give up a worn-out issue, complaining even after previous pain has stopped and harboring disappointments long after they are relevant. We simply cannot make for ourselves a 'new heart' while nursing old grievances. Just as civil wars lend themselves to the passionate preservation of grievances, so civil wars within the soul do the same.' "[7]

Gigi looked up from the book. "It was a moment of truth for Sharon. Tears welled up in her eyes and she quietly asked God to help her forgive Meredith. As she said the words, a warm feeling filled her whole body. And, as they say, the rest is history."

"Gigi, that's not enough! What did she do? Did she call her immediately and apologize? Did she go to her house? What happened? I need to know."

"You're hungry as a mouse sniffing at the cheese, aren't you. Okay, hold on." She was off so quick Lindsey could only grab onto her purse.

"Someone's at the door, Phil. I'll get it," Meredith said as she opened the door.

"Sharon! What a surprise. Come in. Have a seat."

As soon as they sat down the flood gates opened. Sharon began, "Oh, Meredith, I've been so wrong all these years. Will you ever forgive me? Please forgive me."

Tears filled Meredith's eyes and her heart was about to burst. Putting her arms around her daughter-in-law, she said, "My dear sweet Sharon, how I've longed for this moment. Of course I forgive you. And I ask you to please forgive me for having hurt you so long ago."

"Oh, I do, Meredith. I do."

Gigi smiled. "There's nothing more relieving and healing than forgiveness, Lindsey. It's like a cool drink of water in a parched desert."

"Oh, Gigi, thank you for showing me the happy ending to this story."

"My pleasure, dear. I wish all endings could be like this one, but, alas, it isn't always the case."

❀❀❀

In a subdued voice Gigi said, "One of the most difficult situations I've ever seen regarding forgiveness happened to a woman I know named Abby. Her husband Ted was basically ignored as a child. After his parents divorced, his father vanished and he never saw him again. His mother remarried and she and her new husband had a son. The new husband would not accept Ted, but showered affection on his own son. Sadly, Ted's mother joined in the cruel treatment and at age fourteen Ted left home, stayed with relatives and wasn't even missed for a whole month. Through sheer fortitude the poor boy made it through school and on to college. He married Abby and after a few years they adopted a boy they named Alex. About three years later they gave birth to Nathan."

"Thank goodness they had children," Lindsey said. "At least now he could enjoy some happiness. How could anyone treat their own son the way his mother treated him? It's so heartless."

"Indeed it was. Now here's the real tragedy. After Nathan was born Ted's mother became more involved, treating her grandson with great affection. However, their adopted son Alex had no place in his grandmother's heart, nor his step-grandfather's. On visits she would ignore Alex, would not even acknowledge his birthday. However, she would shower Nathan with gifts on his birthday. Whenever Abby and Ted would mention the unequal treatment to her, she would say, 'But Alex is not our blood.' Ted would say, "They're both our sons and we love them equally, and you need to treat them the same." She would then give Alex some small gift to pacify them."

"As if one small gift is going to convince Alex she liked him," Lindsey said. "Kids aren't stupid."

"They all saw right through it. On one occasion Ted's mother invited Alex and Nathan to her house for a special outing. While there, the two boys got in an ordinary sibling argument over a toy hammer they were playing with. The grandmother yanked the hammer from Alex's hands and hit him with it, then locked him in a storage shed out back. They left Alex and she took Nathan on the outing."

"No, Gigi! That's horrible!"

"Nathan was very upset about this and told her it was only a little argument and he wanted his brother to come. She said Alex deserved to be punished and so they went on without him. From that time on a terrible hatred for their grandmother began growing in the hearts of these two boys.

"That was the last straw for Abby and Ted. They could no longer bear the cruel treatment Alex received and they never allowed the boys to go to her house again. When Ted's mother came to their house the boys would leave. They couldn't stand the sight of her," Gigi said.

"I don't blame them. I'd do the same thing," Lindsey said, hardly able to comprehend what these boys were experiencing, especially Alex. "This is awful. Children should find love and comfort from their grandparents. I've always felt safe and loved by my grandparents."

"Every child should. Sadly, it was the opposite end of the spectrum in this family. The hatred wasn't only growing in the boys' hearts, it was growing deep into Abby's. No one treats a mother's child like this without creating a boiling anger, even hatred within her."

"The boys grew up and Alex ended up getting into drugs and made a mess of his life. He had been severely emotionally damaged by the grandmother's cruelties. He was dealing with his own issues over being adopted, and it only fueled his confusion. Even the love of his parents didn't seem to make up for what he was experiencing. So many lives were a wreck because of this cruel woman."

"Oh, Gigi, that makes me so sad for all of them."

"No one quite knew the depth of Ted's suffering from this," Gigi went on. "The anger toward his mother grew like a cancer within him and was magnified by the effects this cruel treatment of the children had on Abby. She became ill and found it difficult to function normally. Ted's mother had created untold misery for his family. At one point he realized the anger was ruining his life and something had to change. He and Abby had become active in church attendance early in their marriage in an effort to find some measure of peace. He was moved by a recent sermon and had jotted down the words that seemed to hit him right in the heart. He practically memorized them.

"Anger is a wasted emotion that eats at your soul. You are the one who suffers, not the one you feel anger towards. Your anger only hurts you and those you love. For this reason when Peter came to Jesus and said, 'Lord, how oft shall my brother sin against me, and I forgive him? till seven times? Jesus saith unto him, I say not unto thee, until seven times: but, until seventy times seven.' "[8]

❀❀❀

"Do you think Jesus knew about Ted's mother when he said it? Maybe she's the exception to the forgiveness rule," Lindsey said in all seriousness.

"No exceptions, Lindsey. It was then that Ted knew he could never change his mother; he could only change himself."

"Did he forgive her?"

"It wasn't an easy process, but through prayer he mustered the courage, went to his mother and told her he forgave her. That didn't mean he condoned what she had done. It simply meant he had handed it over to God and could now be free of the burden of hate and anger. I don't know how much his forgiveness mattered to her, but it made all the difference to Ted. At last he was at peace."

"What about Abby?" Lindsey said.

"It wasn't that easy for her. It took nearly five more years of suffering before she realized that she had to forgive her mother-in-law in order to go on. It took deep soul searching, and finally Abby did as Ted had done. At last she was free of the hatred. Now she simply feels sad for Ted's mother, who is an old, lonely, unhappy woman. They check on her regularly and hope she will one day find her own peace."

"How sad, Gigi. What about their sons? Did they forgive her?"

"Not yet, but I believe the day will come, because they can see the peace it has brought their parents."

"It's so sad that people inflict such misery on themselves," Lindsey said.

"The truth is people are human and they make mistakes, and sometimes horrible things happen in families. In those cases, it seems that prayer is the only sure way to bridge the gap of ill feelings. Let prayer help you keep the window of forgiveness open, Lindsey, and many problems will fly right out that window.

"It's a pretty good practice to keep this particular scripture verse from Matthew in mind: 'For if ye forgive men their trespasses, your heavenly Father will also forgive you.' "[9]

"I guess we're all pretty much in need of being forgiven most of the time," Lindsey said.

"True. To sum it up, my Pertinent Points here are: Give up grudges and be a white-flag waver. Let forgiveness be your best friend. It was Jesus who said, 'Blessed are the peacemakers: for they shall be called the children of God.'[10] That has a mighty appealing ring to me."

One thing was for sure, Gigi was well acquainted with her Bible.

Chapter Five
Window of Patience

 $\mathcal{L}$ indsey had a another worry that was nagging away in the recesses of her mind, and since she was basking in the light of Grandma Grace's wisdom, she thought she might venture forth. "Gigi, I have another concern. Is this a good time to talk about it?"

"Give it to me with both barrels, honey; we got nothing but time."

"Okay. Well, I have a terrific dad, in fact, he's pretty much spoiled me all my life. I grew up hearing him say, 'The Lord has yet to create the man good enough to marry my daughter.' I know it's his way of saying how special I am to him; but now I'm worried."

"Most daddies feel that way," Gigi said. "Nobody's quite up to grade when it comes to their little girl."

"As you probably know, since you seem to pretty much know most everything about me, my dad's a successful engineer and has provided well for our family. This past year since Jeff and I have been seriously dating, he's been in our home a number of times. My mother adores him, and the feeling is mutual. She admires his hard-work ethic and loves his sense of humor. My two younger brothers and little sister Katy think he's the best thing since Mickey Mouse. I'm not sure what my older brother Kevin and his wife Sheri think about him. They've only met him once. As for Dad, well, he seems to . . . tolerate him, and sometimes it isn't even toleration."

"For instance?" said Gigi.

"For instance, a few months ago Jeff was working on some animated drawings for a class project. He's an excellent artist, Gigi. He had come up with some really creative little characters and brought them over to show me and the family. I loved them and so did Mom and the kids. Dad looked at them and said, 'Hmmm. Nice little hobby, but how are you ever going to earn a living with this? If you're interested in my daughter you better start thinking about a career that will pay the bills,' and he walked away. I was mortified! Besides, we hadn't even talked seriously about marriage yet. I could tell Jeff was hurt, but he tried to make the best of it and said, 'Hasn't he ever heard of Pixar?'

"Why did Dad do that, Gigi? He's always taught me to be kind to people, and now look what *he's* doing."

"He's scared," Gigi said. "That's what happens. Dads get scared. Sometimes I think experience has taught them almost too much. They forget how it was when they were young. Maybe a visit to Janet and Bob Griffin might help you understand. Bob's a colonel in the Army. We're going to visit the day when the Griffins flew into the town where their daughter Jeni was going to college. Their sole intent was to get to know her fiancé. They had only met him once when Jeni and Brett came to visit just before they got engaged. Janet and Bob are on their way to pick up the two of them and take them out to dinner."

"I think this is a good idea, Bob," Janet said. "It'll give us a chance to get to know Brett better."

"That one visit was enough for me. It was a real red-flag weekend, Janet. You know very well that I'm less than impressed with him."

"Give him a chance, Bob. He's young and has a lot of growing up to do, but so did we when we got married."

"That's not true. I had set my sights on a degree and was working hard toward it."

"And the semester when we got engaged you failed two classes. And you ended up taking the next semester off. And then 'we' joined the Army. Did you forget about all that?" She laughed.

"This is not about me, Janet! Anyway I worked hard, got that degree and became an officer. But that's beside the point. Times are different now, competition is much more severe, and Brett has no clue."

"Oh, Gigi," Lindsey said, "I'm definitely relating to this." Next thing she knew they were watching the four of them in the restaurant.

"*This is mighty nice of you to take us out to dinner, Colonel Griffin,*" *said Brett.* "*On our budget we usually feast at Burger King.*"

"*We know how that is, Brett. We've walked that road,*" *said Janet.*

"*Not for a long time.*" *Bob said.*

"*It's so wonderful to see you again, Mom and Dad.*" *Then, looking back to the menu, Jeni said,* "*I think I'll have the salmon.*"

"*Me, too,*" *said Janet.* "*What would you like, Brett?*"

"*Uh, well . . . what are you having, Colonel?*"

"*The New York steak.*"

"*Sounds good. Me, too,*" *said Brett.*

The waiter took their order and Bob went right to work on Brett. "*So what are your plans, boy?*"

Jeni flinched, and Lindsey could only imagine that the poor girl's worst fears were about to be realized.

"*He's going to graduate in business,*" *she said.*

"*I asked the boy, Jeni, not you.*"

"*Dad, he's not a boy. His name is Brett, in case you forgot. And he's about to be your son-in-law.*"

"*Humpf,*" *he said with that mean tone in his voice.* "*So, Brett, what're your plans?*"

"*Well, I got a bit of a late start in school, but I'm taking two classes now and working part-time construction for a building company. And . . . uh . . . Jeni's right, I'm thinking about a business major,*" *Brett said, obviously feeling very uncomfortable.*

"Thinking about and doing are two very different things. How are you going to make it happen? Bob said looking straight on at poor Brett. "If you're going to marry my daughter, you darn well better have a plan to take care of her."

"Well, I do have a plan, sir. Next semester I'll be back in school full-time. I can keep my part-time job and, in fact, I'm due for a raise there."

"And, Dad, I graduate next year and can get a good job to help us while Brett finishes," said Jeni with a big smile of confidence.

Fortunately the salads arrived. Trying to change the subject Janet said, "Well, this looks good. Nothing quite like a good tossed green salad, I always say."

"Yeah," said Bob, "but nowadays all you get is a pile of tossed green weeds."

"I think it's somebody's joke on the consumers," said Brett, trying his best.

"I don't think it's funny," Bob retorted, in his usual unkind manner.

After more forced, unpleasant conversation, Brett finally took Jeni's hand and said, "Colonel Griffin, the bottom line is, I love your daughter very much and I intend to take good care of her."

"You better, young man, or you'll have me to answer to."

"Gigi, what kind of a start is that to a marriage?" She was disgusted.

"Terrible," Gigi said. "And I don't know why any in-law would do such a thing, except a worried one. But this kind of worrying is akin to pushing a hog in the mire while all the time saying 'Don't you dare go in that mire.' It doesn't work."

"What happened to them?" She had to know.

"They got married and Bob's worst fears were realized. Brett plugged away at school, kind of piecemeal, while Jeni finished school and then worked. Soon after that, baby number one made her appearance. Jeni cut back on her work schedule to be home with the baby and Brett quit school and went full-time working construction, with the idea of completing his education later. When their second baby was born, his plans were set back even further.

"While this was going on, the Colonel kept telling his daughter, 'I told you so. I told you he wouldn't amount to anything.'"

"Why didn't Jeni stick up for her husband?" Lindsey asked.

"She did on some occasions, but she knew her dad. Standing up to him would be like bravely standing on a busy freeway with a fully-loaded semi bearing down on you — not smart. So she avoided saying anything. Instead she just changed the subject or left the room when he started saying insulting things about Brett."

"You'd think her dad would get some kind of message from that," Lindsey said.

"Never registered."

"How did Brett handle it?"

"Actually, he was quite amazing. He was an easy-going guy, just took it in stride. He didn't want to cause trouble, but in his mind he kept thinking, *Someday he's going to see that he was wrong about me.* He knew the Colonel had a good side to him—after all, he'd helped them when they moved, more than once, giving them 'what for' most of the time, but he helped. And Brett knew the Colonel loved his daughter and she loved him back, in spite of his out-of-control tongue. Besides, Brett didn't want to hurt Jeni by saying something he'd regret."

"Is that a good thing, Gigi? What about setting boundaries? Shouldn't Jeni have set some boundaries here? After all, he was *her* father."

"In effect she did every time she changed the subject or left the room. She did it the way she felt she had to, mostly to avoid hurting her mother. If she had said the wrong thing her father would have exploded and the visits might have stopped, and her mother would have been the one catching the bullet, so to speak. So Jeni did what worked for her, and showed an incredible amount of patience with her dad . . . and her husband."

"What do you mean . . . and her husband?"

"Deep down she believed in Brett. She knew he had it in him to finish school and make his dreams come true. Besides that, he was an incredible daddy to their two little children. She wouldn't have traded that for any stack of money. So she waited and enjoyed what she had."

"Did he ever go back to school?"

"One day after a hard day of working a backhoe, he was stretched out on the sofa . . . tired. In fact, he was sick and tired. Sick and tired of the whole thing. This was not at all what he thought he'd be doing at this point in his life, working for a wage that fell short of meeting all their needs, causing Jeni to have to work part-time. That night one of his high school buddies, Cal, was in town and dropped by for a visit. They chit- chatted for a few minutes and then it got interesting. Let's listen in."

"Brett, I didn't quite figure you as a backhoe dude. What happened to all those plans?"

"Life happened. But we're doing okay. It's just not what I originally had in mind. You know, graduation, a good job . . . like you. But, well, it just didn't happen."

"Do you still want it?" Cal asked.

"Course I do. It just seems out of reach now, with a family and all."

Cal leaned forward in the chair and got real serious. "A college counselor told me something once that made all the difference for me. I was struggling for awhile myself. She said to me, 'Five years is going to come and go in your life, Cal. You have the choice to determine what's going to be waiting for you at the end of that five years. You can be doing the same thing you're doing now and getting nowhere, or you can spend that next five years in school, with a whole list of better prospects at the end of it. The five years are going to come and go regardless of what you do, so you might as well make the most of them.' She got me in gear, Brett, and man, am I glad."

"Five years?" Brett said.

"Yeah, five years. Three to finish up my Bachelor's and two to get a Master's. And it paid off big time. So what are you going to be doing in five years?" Cal asked.

"I don't know."

"Well you might as well be the master of those five years instead of the slave. If I can do it, you can do it."

Gigi picked up where they left off. "After Cal left, Brett had a long talk with Jeni. It all made sense. The time was right. Remember, 'to everything there is a season, and a time to every purpose.' It was Brett's season. Together he and Jeni worked out a plan for him to return to school. It was a big sacrifice for them, but they were determined. And they did it. Now let's look in on them seven years later. Jeni's parents have come for a visit a few months after they were settled in their new house."

"Welcome to our home, Mom and Dad," Brett said, giving them a big hug.

"I've really been looking forward to your visit." Jeni said, taking their coats. "It's been awhile."

"Too long," her mother said. "Of course, any time is too long to be away from my adorable grandkids. Where are they?"

"They'll be home from school any minute now," said Jeni. "I was hoping they'd beat you here. They're so excited to see you."

They walked into the large family room. Taking it all in, Bob folded his arms across his chest and said, "Well, well, well. Now this is a mighty fine place. You sure as heck surprised me, boy . . . uh, Brett. Graduated from college and all. Well, well, well."

"Thank you sir, "Brett said. "It feels real good to be on this end of it."

"No question about it, Bob was impressed," said Gigi. "The house was not extravagant, but very nice. Exactly what his new job could afford."

"And what was his new job?" I asked.

"He got his degree in business and went on for an MBA. Now he's an assistant manager for a very large and successful construction company."

"You mean those years of construction work paid off?"

"Indeed they did. When it came to the interviews there were several qualified candidates, but none of the others had quite the down-in-the-trenches experience that Brett had. It swung the pendulum, and he got the job."

"That is so cool, Gigi."

"Funny thing is, now the Colonel goes around bragging about what a great son-in-law he has. People just need to remember that life requires patience. Things evolve. And that doesn't mean everybody has to have a masters degree to do well. It just means that some need the time to discover what will work for them. And the sooner the parents-in-law learn the skill of tongue-biting the better off they are. I always say, why not enjoy the ride instead of hacking away at it like some lumberjack with a dull ax, never felling the tree, just annoying it to death."

"Do you think my dad will be like Colonel Griffin? Oh, Gigi, I hope not, but it looks a little like he might."

"Don't worry so much about your dad being like the Colonel, just think more about you being like Jeni. You can't control him. You can only control yourself."

She had heard *that* before. It gave her something to think about, and while she was doing the pondering, as related to her own situation, she realized Gigi hadn't finished with this window.

❀❀❀

"Let's explore this concept a little further. Tell me about your brother Kevin's wife," she said.

"I haven't had a chance to get to know her very well. When they come to visit I'm often gone with my job, but when I am there I find it hard to get close to her. It's like there's a little wedge between us that I can't quite define. But I figure she's got to be a pretty nice person or Kevin would not have married her. I just can't put my finger on it."

"Don't forget, this window is all about patience, about giving time for relationships to develop," Gigi said. "And sometimes the developing is hard to come by. I'm going to show you a rather extreme case, just to open your mind to any future happenings in your own family or with people you may know. After all, you've got four siblings, which means you'll likely have four siblings-in-law."

"That's true. I probably will."

In a flash they were in another house listening in on yet another conversation that Lindsey felt wasn't any of their business. Gigi must have read her mind.

"It's okay that we're here. The business of learning from others belongs to us all. Anna is getting more than an earful during a phone call from her daughter, Susan, who is insanely jealous of Jason's wife Caitlyn. Jason's her younger brother, just so you've got the birth order in place."

Susan was launching her attack. "Caitlyn walks around in her high fashion garb, thinking she's heaven's gift to the world!"

"Please don't talk that way about your sister-in-law, Susan. I would hardly call her wardrobe high-fashion, she gets most of it at discount stores and just happens to have a good sense of thrift and style, which is a blessing."

"I can't stand the sight of her!"

"Susan! Stop it!"

"You and Dad just don't get it . . . you think she's so . . . so precious!" she said with angry sarcasm. "You act like she's your daughter, not your daughter-in-law. Well, I think she's a big phony."

"How can you say such a thing? She's Jason's wife, and he would be crushed to hear you talk like this about her. What has she ever done to you to deserve this kind of treatment?"

"Oh, she's done plenty! Every time I buy something new she has to go out and buy something better. And it's not just clothes. When I redecorated my kitchen she came to see it, gushed all over it and then stole a lot of my ideas for her own stupid kitchen."

"You should be complimented that she liked what you did. Imitation is the best form of flattery," Anna said, trying to put a positive spin on the problem.

"And another thing. From the day Jason was born you always favored him. He can do no wrong in your eyes, and now neither can his wife. The whole thing reeks and I'm sick of the stench!"

"That's not true. I never favored Jason over you. We gave you everything, and this is the gratitude we get?" Now Anna was upset.

"I can't talk to you," Susan yelled. "All you do is stick up for Jason and his 'precious' little stinking wife! Well, I hate her, and I hate you, too!" With that Susan slammed down the receiver. Anna looked stunned, and hurt beyond words.

Gigi said, "Anna has dealt with these volatile eruptions from Susan for a long time. Now her anger seems to be coming down on Caitlyn like golf-ball size hail. She'd always been the troublemaker in the family, but this reaction seemed to be the worst yet."

"What causes a person to act like that, Gigi?"

"In her case, and in many others I've known, it's a serious chemical imbalance."

"Isn't that easily corrected with medication?"

"Sometimes, but not always 'easily', and it requires a determined patient. For example, Susan's been on medication for it, but the problem is as soon as she levels out she doesn't think she needs it anymore, stops taking it and the cycle starts all over.""So what can be done?"

"First of all, boundaries need to be set by her mother. Too many times when people have a chemical imbalance, or any other physical problem for that matter, parents and others tend to excuse bad behavior because they think the person can't help it. That's simply not true. It may be difficult, but they *can* help it. Another thing that can be done is to show genuine empathy by walking beside them emotionally without standing on a soap box waving your finger in their face."

"Okay," Lindsey said, "first show me how her mother could possibly empathize with her daughter's hateful comments. You can't agree with the kind of statements Susan was making. That's just not right."

"Showing empathy doesn't mean you agree. You may, but it doesn't mean you do, especially if what they're saying is against your own values. It just means you are listening and trying your best to understand from their point of view. That's why you must combine understanding and empathy with boundaries. Not long after that, Anna learned these concepts and was ready to put them into practice."

"I bet I know where she learned it. She was listening to the radio," Lindsey said with a grin and a wink.

"Maybe. Anyway she learned it," said Gigi. "Let me show you how she made it work for her. They're on the phone and Susan is being her own hateful self again."

"Mom, Caitlyn was just here bragging about their perfect children. Kelli got straight A's on her report card . . . again! Do I care? No! She's just trying to make my kids look dumb. Made me sick to my stomach," Susan said.

"Oh," was all Anna said.

"Just 'Oh'? That's it?" said Lindsey, wanting more.

"That's right. And I could give her a star on her forehead for it," said Gigi. "When you respond with Oh then there's nowhere to go with an argument. Very smart."

Susan went on, "She was here picking up their wheelbarrow that we borrowed last fall. We were going to bring it back, we just hadn't got around to it yet. She probably thinks we were trying to steal it. Who'd want that ugly piece of junk, anyway."

"Hmmm," said Anna, letting her know she was still listening without adding one whit either way to the complaints.

"So you probably think our kids are dumb, too, don't you?"

"No, in fact I think they're both quite talented."

Gigi interjected, "Anna wasn't about to let her grandchildren be put down.

"You're going too far, Susan."

"Too far?" Susan's voice was hitting a higher pitch now. "Oh, you just don't get it. You are so stupid!"

"Anna could plainly see her daughter was skipping rope with the devil, and she wasn't about to join in," Gigi said. "Listen how she handled it."

"Susan, I will be happy to talk with you when you want to treat me with respect. Until then, goodbye," she said firmly and respectfully, and then hung up the phone.

"Now that's setting a boundary!" Gigi said, basking in the light of someone drawing on her wisdom. "She didn't stoop to her daughter's level and yell back, or get defensive, which would only have made the climb out more difficult.

She just stated what needed to happen if her daughter wanted to talk to her, and respectfully said goodbye. A few days later she called her daughter as she normally would— that's the key: treat them normally after setting a boundary and don't withdraw."

"I'm guessing she got a cool reception," Lindsey said.

"Like an ice cube. But Anna ignored it and went on as normal asking about the children and such things. The ice melted and Susan eventually warmed up a little. The best part is, Susan never spoke to her mother that way again. If she had, Anna was ready to repeat the process. Try as she might, though, Anna just couldn't seem to find a way to have a close relationship with her daughter, and that brought a lot of sadness to her. The harsh feelings between Susan and her sister-in-law persisted. It got so bad that Caitlyn and Jason wouldn't come to their home if Susan was there because she would say such hurtful things to them."

"What do you do in a case like this?"

"You keep the window of patience open, and you pray and wait. Anna had a scripture from Proverbs on her refrigerator door that gave her comfort. It said, 'Rest in the Lord, and wait patiently for him.'[11] She knew she was powerless in solving this problem. So she waited."

"Do problems like this ever get resolved, Gigi?"

"Sometimes and sometimes not. At times we just have to patiently endure our whole lives and go on as best we can. A long time ago I knew a daughter-in-law who waited through twenty-five years of disrespectful treatment from her mother-in-law, all the while treating her with kindness.

When the mother-in-law was dying and needed care, who stepped up to the plate? Her daughter-in-law. She was remarkable! Before she died, the mother-in-law apologized to her daughter-in-law from the depth of her heart for the way she had treated her. It was one of those death-bed repentance scenarios. That was a long time ago, and the daughter has now also passed on. There's no question here as to which one of these two women stepped into heaven with a clear conscience.

"But now back to our story. Anna waited patiently for almost eight more years. Then something sudden and surprising happened. Anna's sister, Ashley, who had always shown a special interest in Susan, got terminal cancer and after a few months passed away. Susan adored her aunt and was terribly distraught over her death. She came to the viewing and the funeral and to the family dinner afterward at her cousin's house. She mostly just quietly observed what was happening at these events. About a week later she stopped by to visit Anna."

"Mom, I'm so sad about Aunt Ashley's passing," Susan said to her mother. "I really loved her."

"So did I, sweetheart, and I miss her terribly."

"I watched her family at the funeral," Susan said, "and I don't think I've ever seen such love shown to anyone as her children showed to their father and to each other. Mom, they just took such good care of each other, and were so tender in the things they said and did."

"Yes, it was very touching. They are a close family."

"I want that for our family, Mom. We don't have that . . . and it's . . . it's because of . . . me."

Anna was shocked at this new awakening, but said nothing. Just listened.

"It's my fault and I'm going to change. We don't know what might happen in our family and we need to be there for each other just like they are. I'm going to be a good friend to Caitlyn and Jason from now on. I'm going to be a better daughter to you and Dad. I'm going to build some bridges and make peace in our family."

Susan threw her arms around her mother and they wept with the purest kind of love for each other.

It was one of the sweetest things Lindsey had ever seen, but she wondered how real it was. "Did it last, Gigi? Did she really change?"

"Dramatically. At family gatherings they started to enjoy each other's companionship like never before. Susan does kind and loving things to all members of her family now and has kept the promise she made those many years ago. She completely changed and her change has changed the dynamics of the whole family. And she's a much happier person as a result. She still has her chemical imbalance and sometimes it gets the best of her, but never to the point that she hurts her family because of it. Patience paid off for all of them."

"It sounds like we can choose to be patient or impatient while unpleasant things are happening," Lindsey said, giving serious thought to what she had just learned.

"If things are going to take time, and they usually do, then it's a whole lot smarter to spend that time being patient," Gigi said. "To do otherwise is like continuously pouring alcohol on an open sore without any thought of giving it time to heal on its own. It makes for one continual, unrelenting sting. Healing is on its own timetable and can't be rushed. The good book says, 'Let us run with patience the race that is set before us.'[12]

"So my Pertinent Points here are: be willing to wait for a good relationship to happen, and give family members and in-laws time to grow into who they are in the process of becoming."

Chapter Six
Window of Acceptance

$\mathscr{L}$indsey said, "Gigi, I have a cousin who's married to a man of a different race. She's white as they come and he's as black as night, straight from Nigeria. And he's a fabulous guy. My family adores him, but her problem is that her parents just can't come to grips with the difference."

"That leads us right into our next window, and I'm going to open it wide. This kind of issue can cause a lot of problems with in-laws and end up ruining perfectly good marriages. I've heard it said that even though marriages are made in heaven, man is responsible for the maintenance. I believe that this kind of maintenance is the duty of all of us—not just the couple, but all of us—including the in-laws. Marriage is sacred and we've got to do everything in our power to preserve it and help make it good."

Lindsey was happy about the direction they were going on this one. In her short life she had seen a number of people struggling with accepting differences in the mates their children and siblings married and it always seemed like a waste of emotions to her.

"It's been my belief, Gigi, that once a couple is married, why make an issue of it any more. What's done is done; now make it work."

"Exactly. You're cut out of my cloth, Lindsey girl. Now let's see how this works. We're going to look in on the wedding reception of your cousin, Jennifer, and her brand new husband, Ibrahim. It's a casual gathering, and while Jennifer is visiting with her cousins—I think *you're* in that group—Ibrahim is having a private conversation with a good friend, expressing his feelings."

"This is really odd, Gigi, me seeing me. But there I am, at the reception. This hanging out with you is very strange, indeed."

"Shift your focus to Ibrahim, Lindsey. That's why we're here. Listen."

"I feel very sad that Jennifer's parents would not come to our wedding," Ibrahim said to his friend. "It breaks her heart. They say she has shamed the family by marrying a black man, particularly one from Nigeria."

"That's really sad," his friend said. "I know Jennifer loves you very much. If her parents were not living so far away they could have become better acquainted with you and everything would have been different."

"My plan is to win them over with courtesy toward them and love for their daughter. I will treat them as though they respect me, even if they don't yet."

"I have never known a finer man than you," his friend said. "It may take time, but when they get to know you, they will respect and love you. Everyone who knows you feels that way about you. Ibrahim, Jennifer has married a fine man. Her parents will learn that one day." He embraced his friend.

Lindsey was touched by these words of hope from one friend to another, and wished that she could help Jennifer's parents see the light more quickly.

"Don't forget, Lindsey, relationships take time to develop and bloom. When people water the seed and give it the sunshine of love, they eventually win over those who are dealing with unfounded prejudices. It goes back to the windows of patience and forgiveness; this kind of relationship takes time and a forgiving heart on everyone's part."

"Will it turn out okay, Gigi? Can you show me their future?"

"I wish I could take you there, but I don't have that power. Futures must first be lived. However, because of the type of couple they are I can pretty much predict a positive outcome."

"Me, too, Gigi. When I shut my eyes I can see them a few years down the road with a couple of cute little kids, visiting Jennifer's parents. And I see those grandparents hugging those little children and welcoming Ibrahim into their home with open arms. He's such a good and kind person that they won't be able to resist."

"Well spoken! Love takes away color blindness. Sunshine will follow the dark night. Like the Psalmist said, '. . . weeping may endure for a night, but joy cometh in the morning.'[13]

"Though it may take time, it's inevitable in cases like this. You'll see it at some point in time. One of the fun things about growing old is that you get to see the happy endings."

"Gigi, you never cease to amaze me with your wisdom," Lindsey said. "I feel like I'm hanging out with a full-fledged, honest-to-goodness guru."

"Slow down with the compliments, honey. Gotta keep my humility meter intact or who knows what might happen.

"Now back to business. I told you this window was going to open wide," she said. "So let's take a look at a few more situations where acceptance is the ace of spades in the hand you're dealt."

❀❀❀

Next thing Lindsey knew, they were on a university campus observing a young couple sitting on a bench in a secluded grove of trees. It had to be spring because daffodils and pansies were in full bloom in a nearby garden, drinking in the late afternoon sun that filtered through the trees. It was a quiet, romantic setting. However, the couple looked troubled. The girl was nervously twisting the diamond ring on her finger.

"Chad," the young woman said as she looked down at her ring, *"I know your mother hates me. She knew me through my whole time of trouble. I messed up so bad. Even my foster parents were devastated. I would give anything if I could live the last three years over. Everyone at church knew about my bad reputation, but it was my behavior with . . . he was such a good young man, and everyone knew and respected him. I dragged him down and brought a terrible shame upon him and myself. Yes, he had a part in it, but I purposely did what I did. I tempted him beyond his ability to resist because all I cared about was having a good time. And I've paid a terrible price for it."*

"First of all, Jackie, everyone can resist temptation if they want to," Chad said with a firmness in his voice. *"Believe me, there was no innocent victim here. What you did was wrong, but you need to remember what you just said; you have paid the price. You've repented before God, you confessed your sins, you begged forgiveness, you changed your life. You are a new person. And it's that new person that I fell in love with."*

"How could I ever have done what I did! I hate that I did it. I hate who I am."

"Don't talk like that. I know who you are—you're a daughter of a Heavenly Father who loves you. I'm going to ask you a serious question, Jackie. Do you believe in Jesus Christ and that He atoned for our sins?"

"Of course I do. With all my heart I do. That's what's made me into a new person, but the old one still haunts me."

"Then take the next step; don't just believe in Christ, but believe Him. He said that He paid the price for all of our transgressions. Believe Him. He already suffered for the sins of mankind, including yours, and that means you don't have to suffer any more because you

truly repented. Do you understand that, Jackie? Listen to what He said."

Chad had come prepared. He pulled a small New Testament out of his backpack. The place was marked and he began, "Right here in Hebrews Jesus said, 'I will be merciful to their unrighteousness, and their sins and their iniquities will I remember no more.'[14] Did you get that, Jackie, He will remember your sins no more. I hope you can find comfort in that fact. You have been forgiven and, I'm going to say it again, He will remember your sins no more." He set the book down and tenderly took her in his arms.

"I do know that," she said, finding comfort in his embrace. "I just hope your mother can forgive me someday and remember them no more."

"She will. It'll take some time, but she'll see who you've become and she won't be able to resist loving you any longer. She's a good woman; she's just scared for me."

"Gigi, I find it interesting how 'scared' parents too often mess it all up," Lindsey said, feeling wise again.

"It's normal for parents to be scared, Lindsey. It's because they love their children. But because they love their children they also need to trust them."

Their attention was back to the couple.

"I'm scared for you, too," Jackie said. "I'm turning your family against you by marrying you."

"Hey, no more talk like that. I'm a big boy and I know what I'm doing, and right now I know I'd better be getting to class." With that they took each other by the hand and quickly walked away.

"What happened to them, Gigi, or is that still in the future?"

"No, that was about fifteen years ago, and a lot of bread has been baked in that oven. They had a small wedding without a lot of fuss. Chad's mother didn't come, but his father did. His mother held a grudge for a few years, which is so sad and basically stupid. Grudges are a mighty heavy burden to carry around. Never did make sense to me, but oh well, some people just have to grow out of it. Carrying grudges is like wearing an old, ragged coat year after year when a new one's hanging right in your closet the whole time.

"Well, Chad's mother finally decided to put on the new coat. She got the picture that Jackie loved her son with all her heart and was absolutely faithful to him. Besides that, Jackie treated her mother-in-law in a loving manner, no matter how she treated her. You can turn that kind of love away for just so long. Now she praises Jackie for being such a good wife for Chad and such a good mother to their four children. All I can say is that it has all the earmarks of a truly happy ending. An ending that could have started at the beginning if Chad's mother had played the card of acceptance right from the start."

That made Lindsey think. She was beginning to figure things out. She realized that she needed to accept Jeff's mother for who she is and allow them both time to grow into a loving relationship. That wouldn't rule out challenges, but it meant she could love her all along the way, not just later.

❀❀❀

"Acceptance comes in all different forms," said Gigi. "I want you to watch this scene with me. It'll warm your heart, particularly after what we've just seen. Off we go."

Before Lindsey knew it they were surrounded by shelves of books of every kind, with people speaking in whispers. It had to be a library. A kindly man was directing some teenagers to a certain book. The way he was so much "in the know" indicated he must be a librarian. Off to the side, skimming through a *National Geographic* was a woman in a wheelchair. She kept glancing at the man, in a kind of admiring way. She looked to be about thirty-five—nice-looking woman, wearing on her left hand what appeared to be an engagement ring. In a different part of the room another woman, much older than she, was talking with someone who obviously was a friend.

"That's Ellen, the librarian's mother," Gigi said, pointing to the other woman. "She was with the woman in the wheelchair, until she saw her friend come in. Let's listen in on their conversation."

"We're getting good at this," Lindsey said.

"Joyce, I can't tell you how happy I am for Joseph. I swear I wondered if that boy would ever get married, and now here he is at forty-two engaged to a wonderful woman! And he's happy as a clam."

"Doesn't it concern you that he's marrying someone who is . . . well, handicapped? Isn't that her in the wheelchair over there?" Joyce said.

"That's her all right, and isn't she lovely? Her name is Justine, and he couldn't have found a more wonderful woman. She's a school teacher, and you should see her with her students. They adore her. Come and I'll introduce you to her."

"You don't seem concerned at all about her disabilities," Joyce said as they walked toward Justine.

"Why would I be? She's loaded with many more a-bilities and they far exceed any disabilities she may have. If all people were as capable as she the world would be a much better place."

As they walked toward the woman in the wheelchair she said, "Justine, I want you to meet my friend, Joyce."

Justine immediately gave Joyce a warm handshake. "How nice to meet you. I love meeting friends of my soon-to-be family."

"I've heard lovely things about you," Joyce said, warming right up; Justine's friendliness was contagious.

"Well, it looks like Joseph's finished," Ellen said. "The three of us are going to lunch and we'd better get going. It was nice running into you, Joyce. Look for a wedding announcement in the mail soon."

"This is a woman who has honored her son's choice in a mate and has completely and unconditionally accepted her," Gigi said. "She's found every reason in the world to love her. When you fill your mind with positives about a person, there's less room for the negatives."

❁❁❁

"Wouldn't it be nice if all in-laws could do this?" Lindsey said. "But for some reason it's just not that easy for some people. One of the secretaries at my work, a woman several years my senior, was pouring her troubles out to me on one of our breaks. She said her son-in-law will not accept their lesbian daughter because he's repulsed by her lifestyle. If she's at a family event he won't come. It really hurts her. Sometimes I get confused about this issue too, Gigi. I'm a fairly open-minded woman, but I still have some questions in my own mind. So when someone hits me with a problem like this, I'm pretty much up a tree as to what to say. I could use a little insight."

"Being open-minded doesn't mean you have to agree with everyone's sexual preference, Lindsey. You need to decide where you stand on this issue as related to your own beliefs. Then, because you are a person who respects others, no matter who they are, you will treat them with respect and kindness. That's where people get this all mixed up. They think that because they don't condone a certain lifestyle, they must ostracize themselves from any association with a person who is living it. Sally Fisher is dealing with this same issue. Her son Conley is gay. Let's pay her a visit."

Sally and Conley were working together in her backyard garden. He was spading up the soil and she was following after, raking it smooth and ready for planting.

"Thanks so much for coming over to help me, Conley. I know you're busy with your job and everything, so I really do appreciate your taking the time to help. Dad won't be back for another week and I know he'll help me then, but with the weather so perfect right now I just needed to take advantage of it and get going."

"No problem, Mom. I know the story of the Little Red Hen; you taught me well. I can almost taste the fruits of this garden already."

"So does that mean you'll be back here planting, weeding and harvesting?"

"Absolutely! You know I've always enjoyed gardening. You can count on my help whenever you need it."

"Thanks, son. How's your job going?"

"Great. Becoming an architect was the smartest thing I ever did. I really enjoy my work," Conley said.

"You always had a talent for art," said his mother. *"And I often wondered where it would lead you."*

"Right now we're designing a large apartment building, and I'm coming up with some creative ideas that will distinguish it from the ordinary run-of-the-mill types."

"I'll be interested in seeing it when you're done. I'm proud of the way you've developed your career, Conley."

"Thanks, Mom. That means a lot to me."

"You need to know," Gigi said, "that the Fishers are not pleased with Conley's homosexual lifestyle. It hangs in the background of their minds like an aching tooth they can't pull out. It flies in the face of everything they believe. However, they love their son and decided that, though they didn't agree with some of his choices, they could love him without loving those choices."

"She isn't discussing that issue with him at all," Lindsey said. "I couldn't help but notice how she praised him for his talent. She seems to genuinely care about him and the success he's having professionally."

"Like I said, she loves him, and she wants him to know it. But the real problem they face is similar to your co-worker's. They have a son-in-law, Neal, who won't have anything to do with Conley because he's gay."

"I think that's sad."

"Me, too."

"So what's Neal's problem?"

"Let's visit him in his home and you'll find out. He's having a discussion, a rather intense one, with his wife, Megan."

In one quick second, there they were in Neal and Megan's home, like flies on the wall, taking it all in without a twinge of conscience on Gigi's part.

"Neal, I think you need to put aside your prejudices and accept my brother for who he is," said Megan.

"I don't agree with how he lives, and I don't want our children associating with him."

"That is so ridiculous. He's their uncle and they need to know him. He's a very loving person, and you'd find that out if you just gave him a chance."

"Megan, you don't understand how critical this is."

"Okay, how critical is it?" she said with an edge in her voice.

"I haven't told you this, but one of my client's sons . . . well, he's gay, too. At least he was. Now he's dead. My client broke down yesterday and told me what happened. I didn't say anything to you about it because I didn't want to hurt you. He contracted AIDS through an infected partner and suffered an agonizing death."

"It's fear! It's that scared-parent thing again, isn't it!" Lindsey said, having a new realization.

"That's right. He fears that if his children associate with Conley they will think it's cool to be gay, and that they might adopt that lifestyle themselves, or at the very least experiment with it. Neal's been quietly studying the research on this subject and the statistics are pretty frightening, particularly regarding health problems and life expectancy.[15] He's just plain scared for his kids," said Gigi.

"So what's the solution?"

"They need to take the bull by the horns, so to speak, and teach their children the facts—then love them and trust them to live their values and be kind to all people. Jesus set the pattern. He said, 'Love one another as I have loved you.' He doesn't have conditions on His love. He certainly has rules to live by, but the breaking or keeping of those rules seems to have little to do with the fact that He loves us all. So it's all about acceptance of the person, not necessarily the lifestyle. No good comes from going around avoiding everybody who isn't just like you. That's a heavy hat to wear.

"Let's go get another view of how acceptance works in a different situation."

❀ ❀ ❀

There they were in the back yard of a middle-class neighborhood, just Lindsey and her sweet little old lady wizard. They were sitting on someone's deck in a glider swing, gently swaying back and forth.

"I always wanted one of these swings," Lindsey said. "We never had one when I was growing up, but Jeff's mother has one, and Jeff and I like to sit in it and talk . . . when his mother's not there. I'm going to have one of these when I have my own home. Jeff likes them, too. There's something comforting about rocking."

"I knew it. This can be a good marriage; you both want a glider swing. See, you don't have a thing to worry about."

"You're being silly, Gigi. Why are we here?"

"There's another thing you and Jeff have going for you—you share the same religious beliefs. It always troubles me why anyone would marry a person of another faith, particularly if one or both are devout in that faith. But it happens all the time. I think it harkens back to that 'love is blind' thing. Problem is, people don't stay blind and it can be such a huge problem down the road, particularly when children come along and each wants them raised in his or her religion. But we'll get to that in a minute. First, back to the fact that you and Jeff are of the same faith."

"That's an important criteria for the man I marry."

"Good. However, you and Jeff were not raised in the same home, and you each grew up with different ways of living your religion, even if it's the same religion. Differing traditions can cause a little rift with the in-laws."

"What do you mean? We both go to church on Sundays, we both believe in the Bible and we both say our prayers. Sometimes we even pray together," she defended.

"I know, and I'm glad to hear it. Now let's get specific. Do you know what Jeff and his mother do on Easter Sunday?"

"Actually, we've never been together at Easter time. What do they do?"

"They have a tradition that has been handed down for several generations. They dress up in their best Easter clothes and go to morning worship service and then meet with aunts, uncles and cousins at his grandparents' home where they have a quiet dinner, always a big rib roast with all the trimmings. After dinner they sing hymns and share stories of how Christ has blessed their lives throughout the year and express their gratitude to Him. They stay in their nice clothes, listen to appropriate music and treat the day as sacred, all day long."

"I didn't know that," Lindsey said. "That's nice, but not at all like we do it. We all go to church and then run into the house so we can change out of our Sunday clothes. Then we start looking for our Easter baskets that Dad hid, under the direction of the Easter Bunny, of course. After we find our baskets, which are full of all kinds of treats, we run outside for our Easter egg hunt. This is really fun because we know Mom and Dad have hidden dollar bills in some of the plastic ones. It gets a little wild and crazy and is so much fun. The little kids love it—in fact, we all love it. Then we go on a picnic and just laugh and play the whole rest of the day. And our family and their parents have done these things for as long as we can remember."

"So which way will you and Jeff do it when . . . if . . . you get married? Remember, this window is about acceptance.

Will you accept his way or will he accept your way, or is there another alternative?"

"Hmmm. That just might be our first fight. That would really please Jesus on Easter, wouldn't it," Lindsey said facetiously.

"Keep in mind that his mother will be inviting you to participate in their family tradition, and your parents will be inviting you to participate in theirs. So how are you going to resolve this?"

"I can see a mother-in-law problem popping up here in bright red lights. I'm not going to make our kids sit around somber all day long, Gigi. Does his family do anything with the Easter bunny?"

"No, they think it's too pagan."

"You're kidding! Jeff and I haven't even talked about Easter—not that I thought we needed to!" she said, feeling really sorry for their future kids if she married Jeff.

"So what do we do, Gigi?"

"What do you think will work?" They sat there silent for a few minutes, just rocking while Lindsey was pondering the options.

"Does compromise have anything to do with acceptance?" she asked.

"I'd say just about everything,"

"Okay, I can see that Jeff and I would need to talk about these kinds of things and figure out what will work for us, maybe take a few things from each of our family traditions and create our own."

"That's exactly how it will work, Lindsey. You can have your own way of celebrating and invite your families to your home, and you can also participate in part or all of your families' celebration in their homes. You can pick and choose, and if you do the choosing in advance so parents and in-laws know what to count on and are included in some way, it will work. Then it becomes their duty to accept you and the traditions you have chosen as a new family.

"Incidentally," Gigi said, "I know several families who have a whale of a good time with the Easter bunny and egg hunts on Saturday, and then reserve Sunday for a more serious focus on Jesus and the resurrection. Seems to me to be a good balance. But you'll figure out what will work for you.

"Keep in mind that this is just one of the differences you'll have even though you're of the same faith. Anticipate as many as you can and discuss them in advance, so you can both figure out a compromise and acceptance of each other's traditions. The sooner you do that, the better. As you do this your in-laws, and his, are more likely to respect both of you and accept your choices," she said.

"If there are differences when you share the same faith," Lindsey said, "I can only imagine how hard it is if you don't. Like my Aunt Doris. I haven't seen her for years. They moved away and I only see her and Uncle Walt when they come for reunions, but I've heard about their problems."

"That's why we're here. We're sitting in your Aunt Doris's swing."

"No way! Really?"

"Cross my heart, never hope to die. This is their home."

Lindsey perked up and started looking around at the surroundings. Flowers grew profusely along the back edge of the deck. In the shady areas she identified impatiens of all colors, several groups of hosta plants and some grape holly. In a large bed out in the sun she saw clusters of geraniums, petunias, iris and marigolds. It was beautiful. She knew her plants. In her family they love gardening. It went back to her great grandmother on her mother's side. "This fits, Gigi. This is the kind of yard Aunt Doris would have."

"Good, because it's definitely hers. In fact, gardening brings her a great deal of peace amidst her heartache."

"I know she's had a difficult time with one of her sons, but I really don't know any details. What happened? Is this something I need to know?"

"Let's hope and pray you never face anything like this, and I'm pretty confident you won't. But others do. And whether you do or not, there's an important in-law lesson to be learned." She launched into the story full force.

"Your aunt and uncle were united in their religious beliefs and taught their children well, and in a very loving manner, I might add. All six children grew up to be good members of their church, doing their best to live the teachings of Christ. A Ten Commandments plaque still hangs on the wall in their living room.

"I remember seeing that when I was a little girl, before they moved away."

Gigi went on. "All of the children found mates within their faith, and everything seemed to be going so well. Their son Rulon . . ."

"Oh, Gigi, Rulon was so good looking. I was just a little girl, but I remember how handsome this cousin was. He married a woman named . . . hmmm . . . Kayla, I think. "

"And they had two children," Gigi said. "I don't know if you knew that he's a successful physical therapist—even owns his own clinic. Doris and Walt had concerns about this marriage because Rulon's wife was a little . . . uh . . . cold . . . well, maybe not cold, just not as affectionate as Rulon would have liked. But she was a hard worker and they loved her and the kids and hoped everything would work out well in the end.

"In the meantime, a young, pretty secretary at Rulon's clinic took a liking to him. In fact, it was more than just a liking, it was an outright predator-after-the-prey kind of thing. He enjoyed the attention, and before long the prey became dinner for the evening. She ate him alive. And he succumbed, even though he knew and believed adultery was wrong. The predator's name was Ginny. Her design was not simply to break down his resistance to an affair, but to break up his marriage and convince him to marry her—not only was he handsome, he had money. It was as though he had a ring in his nose and she was leading the bull without résistance. He did her bidding. He divorced his wife, breaking her heart and the hearts of his two children. And his parents' as well. It was a tragedy.

"I have one thing to say about divorce," Gigi said. "It stinks! Unless there's abuse—and in my book that includes unrepentant infidelity—I believe it is one of the most selfish acts in the universe, particularly when there are children involved. So many innocent people suffer."

"Why don't you tell me how you really feel, Gigi?" Gigi didn't laugh, just gave Lindsey that look.

"When the divorce was final Rulon married Ginny. You can only imagine the heartache this brought to your Aunt Doris and Uncle Walt. They were devastated. When something like this happens it presents a whole hamper full of dirty laundry, but I'm only going to address two problems with you right now.

"First, you're young and don't know this yet, Lindsey, but when a couple marries, the parents of the bride generally do all they can to show love and kindness to their new son-in-law, and the same with the groom's parents to their new daughter-in-law. In fact, they go about the work of falling in love with their son's wife or their daughter's husband. And usually they do.

"Can you start to get the picture, Lindsey? Now Rulon is divorced from Kayla, just when Doris and Walt have come to really love and appreciate her, in spite of her not being the perfect wife. But then who is? Goes for husbands, too. So what does divorce do to their relationship with her? Is she a daughter-in-law anymore? She's still the mother of their grandchildren. Does she still call them Mom and Dad? What is she to them now, and they to her? Divorce hurts so many people, and Doris and Walt were hurting to the very core of their beings. They're figuring out that relationship as best they can, trying not to blame Kayla or build walls between her and them for fear of losing their grandchildren."

"Gigi, this just gets so complicated," Lindsey said with a look of consternation on her face.

"Now they're faced with another problem: they have to find a way to fall in love with the predator!" Gigi said.

"No they don't! She doesn't deserve their love." Lindsey said it with a vengeance, and meant it.

"Here's the second thing. When Rulon married Ginny she insisted he leave his church and join hers, which he had to do if they were to be married in the cathedral of her dreams. She would have nothing to do with his parents because she feared they would try to talk him out of the marriage. He was so blinded by her that he left the church he had cherished all his life, the church that his children and his entire family belong to. He ignored the counsel of his parents. Many times Doris sobbed and prayed whole entire days while Walt was at work. Walt shed a ton of his own tears, too. They had to figure out a way to accept Ginny, so they turned to the scriptures for guidance. They came upon one of my favorite verses in Matthew, and it made all the difference.

> " 'But I say unto you, love your enemies, bless them that curse you, do good to them that hate you, and pray for them which despitefully use you, and persecute you;'[16]

"Ginny sure as heck was an enemy to the family at that point," Gigi said. "So they prayed for her, and did everything in their power to show love to her; after all, she was now their daughter-in-law. Time passed, and now Ginny and Rulon have two of their own children, whom Ginny insists be raised in her religion. This infidelity thing just keeps putting knots in the rope. Doris and Walt want to be good grandparents to these little kids, too, and they still love Rulon—he's their son. Ginny now welcomes them into her and Rulon's home, but is determined they know she is not interested in their religion, and has told them in so many words that Rulon has fully converted to hers."

"Oh, this gets so confusing," Lindsey said, shaking her head in disgust.

"Now let's go inside, so you can see your Aunt Doris and Uncle Walt. Remember, they won't see you. Rulon is there visiting them, with some very interesting news. I want you to hear this from the donkey's mouth, so to speak."

"Gigi! Was that nice?"

"Sorry, I repent," she said. "I'm not perfect, you know. Let's listen."

"Rulon, this is a nice surprise," said Doris.

"We always love a visit from you, son. How are Ginny and the children?" asked Walt.

"They're doing fine. The reason I came was to tell you that . . . well, I've made a mess out of my life," Rulon said, struggling to get the words out. "It was a big mistake to leave my family for another woman and then join her religion for convenience sake. It betrayed all I knew to

be right and true, but I did it, and I have to at least now be faithful to Ginny and the kids. She's my wife and I'm not about to destroy another family. What I can't do is hold to her religion when I still believe in my own, so I made the decision to return to my faith . . . our faith, Mom and Dad."

They both threw their arms around him. Then Rulon said, "I don't expect Ginny to join our church since she's solid in her own, so we decided to agree on the fact that we disagree on this subject and will respect each other's choices."

Then came the ultimate question. "What about the children?" Doris asked. "Which church will they attend?"

"We're still trying to work that out, but for now they'll continue going with their mother. When they get a little older they may want to go with me at least some of the time; I hope so. But the good part is that my older children will know I am with them one hundred percent in this area. I know that's going to make them happy. I hope they'll forgive me for what I've done to their lives."

Gigi shook her head and said, "Oh, how some parents complicate the lives of their children. Poor little things are like checkers being jumped over right and left."

"Gigi, it looks to me like Rulon is really trying to do the right thing now."

"Yes, he is. I'll give him credit for that. It's just that I'm hard put to tolerate his infidelity in the first place. But I have to remember that judgment is the Lord's, not mine. It does look like Rulon's trying to put things back together; it's just that it's hard when there are so many broken pieces. We have so keep remembering that it's our duty to forgive and to love."

"This window of acceptance is all about love, isn't it?" Lindsey said.

"Indeed it is. And I would say your aunt and uncle are doing a mighty fine job of it."

Then she realized that this was now her opportunity to use what she had learned about acceptance. "Gigi, I'm Ginny's cousin-in-law! I need to get to know her and show a little family love on my part."

"I'm betting she'd like that, and so would Rulon and your aunt and uncle. You can do this without showing any less love for Kayla and your niece and nephew on that side of the equation. There's one more thing I want to show you about acceptance. We're going to pay another visit to my favorite therapist, Dr. Calhoon."

❀❀❀

Almost instantly they were back in Dr. Calhoon's office. This time he was talking to a nice-looking woman with short, blonde hair. As often seemed to be the case with those visiting Dr. Calhoon, she was crying.

"Doctor, I have tried to fit in with my husband's family, but there doesn't seem to be any way. Is there something wrong with me?" she said.

"What's happening, Angela?" he asked.

"When we go visit James's parents, his family members are coolly courteous but they basically ignore me. I try to join the conversations and they sometimes will make a one word acknowledgment and go on with the conversation as though I wasn't even there."

"That would be hard to take. Is anything else happening?" Dr. Calhoon asked.

"Any time either of his parents or siblings plan an event, the invitation is extended to my husband directly and sometimes our children, and I'm conspicuously left out. When my husband takes me to these events, a good time is had by the family but it seems that the spouses of their children are ignored. At a recent gathering my husband's brother's wife, Trish, and I stood together on the outside of the fun and she remarked to me 'It seems that I'm not included in any of the invitations.' I was shocked to hear that she was experiencing the same thing. My question is, why are they treating us like lepers? I work very hard at being a good wife and mother and a caring daughter-in-law, but that doesn't seem to make any difference."

"This is not the first time I've heard about this type of in-law interaction," Dr. Calhoon said.

"There's something more," Angela said. "The last time we were together they wanted to take a family photo, including the grandchildren. My mother-in-law grouped everybody exactly where she wanted them, and left Trish and me out. When my husband saw this, he said, "But Mother, where do Angela and Trish go?' She turned to him and said forcefully, 'This is a family picture! They're not family.' My husband just backed down and didn't say anything, nor did his brother or his dad, who definitely doesn't wear the pants in this family. My sister-in-law and I were crushed. We both wondered what was wrong with us."

"*There are three types of family interactions, Angela,*" *Dr. Calhoon said. "One is where the parents can hardly wait to get rid of their children. They and their families are pushed out of the parents' lives almost completely. This is known as a centrifugal family, kind of like the whirligigs on a playground that spins around trying to force everyone off.*"

"*Oh, yeah, my kids love those,*" *she said.*

"*And that's right where they belong, on playgrounds, not in family relationships.*

"*The second type of family is where all of the force exerted by the parents is to draw the family tightly under their protective wings. The only ones that are included are direct blood kin, which includes their own children and the grandchildren. That is like centripetal force, that which draws to the center, thus they are referred to as a centripetal family.*

"*The third kind of family, which I call a normal family, is where there is a gentle pushing out of the nest to allow the children to grow up and establish their own families. In this family there is a loving inclusion of the whole family together, including the in-laws. Family members unite on special occasions and foster unity and caring. This is the ideal and involves the gentle forces of both centrifugal and centripetal, and thus the comings and goings happen without any offense and create loving relationships.*"

"*There's no question which one I married into. A king-size centrip . . . how'd you say that?*"

"*Centripetal. A bit of a tongue twister.*"

"*Is there any hope, Dr. Calhoon, or am I just stuck?*"

"*There is hope and here's what has to happen. In order for you to be accepted by this family your husband must set a boundary. He must stand up to his mother in your defense. Often this is a cycle passed down from one generation to the next, but not always. Your husband now has the important responsibility of breaking the cycle or not allowing it to become a cycle. And we can only hope his brother will join him in the effort."*

"James won't listen to me if I tell him to stand up to his mother. We'll just end up in a big argument," Angela said.

"Bring him with you on your next appointment. Do you think he'll come?"

"I don't know. What I do know is that he loves me and he feels bad about this, too."

"Good. Then tell him that together we're going to discover a solution," Dr. Calhoon said.

"He was more than willing to come with his wife," Gigi said. "He and the doctor worked out the dialogue that he would use to set the boundary. James was eager to get the job done and didn't wait until another event. He went to see his mother privately and laid it all out plain and simple. And it took a lot of courage on his part, which speaks highly of him. Wanna see what happened?"

"I wouldn't miss this for anything," Lindsey said, eager to see what fireworks this would set off.

"Why, James! What brings you here?" his mother said, surprised to see him when she opened the front door.

He hugged his mother and didn't waste time on trivialities. "Mother," he said, bolting full steam ahead, "in all our family doings—parties, dinners, pictures and everything — from now on my wife is to be included as a member of our family."

"What do you mean, James? I've always included her."

"No, you haven't. Not by any stretch of the imagination. The most you have done is tolerate her, and it's hurt her deeply. I won't stand for it any longer." Her mouth was gaping open about this time, and he continued with absolute resolve. "When I married Angela she became one of us. And, in case you hadn't noticed, our children are as much hers as they are mine. We are as one, Mother, and must be treated as such.

"If this is not acceptable then my wife, my children and I will not be attending any future family functions. I would hope that would never happen because I love you and Dad and all the rest of the family, but I will not allow my wife to be excluded any longer."

His mother fell back onto a chair and exclaimed, "Well, I never!"

"I hope that 'never' means you'll never exclude her again." He leaned down and kissed her on the cheek and said, "I love you, Mother, and I'm sure this can all work out. We can be one big, happy family. Well, I gotta go. See you later."

And he left, leaving a stunned mother.

"Did it do any good, Gigi?"

"It did. They remembered that Dr. Calhoon had said it would take baby steps for his mother to make such a big change, but to accept those steps while staying true to the boundary."

"Did she ever make the total transition?"

"Pretty close. She actually learned to love Angela, mostly because Angela kept on being kind and respectful to her. Shortly after that, when her mother-in-law had back surgery, she took in a few meals and helped with the household chores. Like I always say, you can turn your back on love just so long."

"How about Trish? Did it spill over onto her?"

"It did, and they're a much happier family now. As you said before, acceptance is all about love.

"So here are my Pertinent Points for this window: When it comes to those who marry into your family it works best to love them just the way they are, differences and all. And, for goodness sakes, don't play favorites.

"Enough of this window, let's move on."

Chapter Seven
Window of Respect

$\mathcal{M}$oving on took them to a small country church nestled in the wooded hills of the Appalachian mountains. As they walked up the stairs leading to the front door Lindsey heard the strains of a familiar tune. A choir of voices filled the air and gave her goose bumps.

"Amazing grace. How sweet the sound, that saved a wretch like me. I once was lost, but now am found; was blind, but now I see."

"This song is about you!" she said, thinking it had a new application. "It's about you, Gigi. You are Amazing Grace, and you're helping me see!"

"Hush, child. Only Jesus is amazing; it's His grace we're honoring here, not me. However, if I've helped you see some things, then I'm happy. That's my purpose."

They sat on the back pew, listening along with a congregation of about a hundred or so other people. It wasn't a big chapel and could barely hold them all. The simple stained glass windows were brilliant against the morning sunlight. It was a radiant setting.

"Why are we here, Gigi? Is this where you go to church?"

"It is today. I want you to hear what the preacher has to say. If you take his message to heart it will serve you well in your relationships with your parents and your future mother-in-law."

"Brothahs and Sistahs, welcome on this beautiful Sabbath mornin'," the preacher began. "Surely the Lord is pleased today that so many of y'all won the war with your mattresses. I do believe a special light shines on those who rise up out of their beds of comfort and come to hear the holy word. And now that you're here, I'll do my best to see that no snorin' takes place." The congregation chuckled.

"Gigi, I think I'm going to like him," she whispered, enchanted with the preachers warm and inviting accent. "From the way these folks are dressed it looks like we've gone back in time."

"Indeed we have. Now shhhh," she said, putting her finger to Lindsey's lips, like she'd done before.

"We've been talkin'," the preacher continued, "'bout the Ten Commandments these past few weeks, and today I'm gonna be addressin' one that seems to get a bit misunderstood on a regular basis. To set the stage, so t'speak, I'm gonna tell you a story.

"It's 'bout me when I was a little feller 'bout ten years old. My pa set me down with my big brother Jake, him bein' 'bout twelve, and said

'I'm gonna make a deal with you boys. See those two calves over yonder? You each git one. Jake, the brown one's yours and, Jed, the black one's yours. You take good care of 'em, feed 'em, water 'em every day jist like I taught you, each one of you takin' care of your own in its separate pen. Then come summer we'll sell 'em off and you pay me fer the feed you used and a few bucks fer the calf and you youngins can keep the rest. Can I count on you? Remember, the deal is you take care of your own. I'm gonna be mighty busy with my own chores so don't be countin' on me lookin' in on ya. Will you take good care of 'em?'

"We promised we would. We was mighty happy 'bout this deal. I worked my head off doin' my best for all of 'bout two whole weeks. Then it got t' be a pain in the you-know-where, and I got busy playin' and fergot 'bout my calf. Pa left it all up to us. Sometimes he'd say t' me, 'You doin' right by that calf, Jed?' I'd say, 'Yeah, Pa,' and I'd quick run out and give it somethin' t' eat. But mostly I just plain fergot 'bout it, or was too lazy, don't know which.

"One day I went out t' the calf pen and there my calf was layin' on the ground . . . deader 'n my great-grandpa in his grave. Here's the hard part. All I could think of was how I'd let my pa down. I'd been t' church, I knew the commandment and at that very instant it ran through my head like a ragin' river: 'Honour thy father and thy mother: that thy days may be long upon the land which the Lord thy God giveth thee.'[17] I had it memorized. I knew it meant I was to honor Pa and Ma by obeyin' them. I had not obeyed Pa in this and I figured that as soon as he found out, my days on this land might be comin' to a halt. I was skeered to the bone. I looked over in the other pen and there was Jake's calf, hale and hearty, and there was mine, a worthless piece a cowhide layin' there, callin' down the wrath of Pa upon me.

"*Well, to shorten this tale, my pa was definitely upset. He didn't whup me, jist give me a penetratin' look of disgust that seared itself into my very soul, and said, 'I'm sorely disappointed in you, son.' That's all he said. Then he took me by the hand and together we buried the poor thing. He made me do extra chores t' work off the feed money, which weren't much since I hadn't used much, and the cost of the calf, which was more. I never fergot that look a' disappointment, and ever after was the most obedient boy a pa could ever want. There ain't no question that a boy's gotta obey his ma and pa and that by doin' so he honors them, jist as the Bible says.*

"*Now here's where it sometimes gets goin' askew. This boy grew up, and I found myself a fine woman t' marry, which I did. All this time, I'm doin' my level best to obey Ma and Pa.*

"*One day Pa's gettin' his nose into our bizness a little bit and my wife is not takin' to it too kindly. We got into a spirited discussion over it and what we didn't know was that Pa was comin' up to our door, but when he heard us goin' after it, he jist waited til we was done. Problem was, he heard my wife say, 'It ain't yer pa's bizness. It's ours.' And I said, 'No matter, I got t' honor Pa by doin' what he says.'*

"*Pa, hearin' this, can't wait no longer and knocks on the door. We shut right up and invite him in to sit a spell, which he does. But he's not sittin' more'n a minute when he says, 'Son, it's time you learnt an important lesson 'bout honorin' me and Ma. That don't mean you hafta do what I says or what Ma says now that you're a man. It means you honor us by listenin' to our ideas and then the two of you run 'em 'round in your own heads to find out if it's what you think is best for your situation. Then you do what's right for y'all, not what's gonna pacify me and Ma.'*"

"'But, Pa,' I said. And he said. 'Listen me out, son. Now that you're a grown-up man the best way you can honor Ma and me is to raise up a honorable family of your own. That's how you live that commandment, not by kowtowin' to our every whim, but takin' your own responsibility and raisin' an upright family. I'd be mighty honored to have that happen, son.'

The preacher wiped the perspiration off his forehead with his handkerchief, then, pointing at the congregation for emphasis, he continued.

"Did you git that, folks? My pa was right. Now I'm strongly suggestin' that y'all get out of your grown-up kids' bizness. When they ask, go ahead and give 'em your wisdom, then butt out and leave the decidin' to them. And you young married folks, listen to your ma and pa, thank 'em for their love and don't go gettin' your dander up, then take what works for you and put the rest aside.

"Now you older folks, you know they might make some mistakes, and if'n they do, that's how they're gonna learn. I'm thinkin' they'll do their best if'n you give 'em a chance. That's the way for them to honor you and for you to honor them. It's called respect. And we all need to give it to one another."

There were a lot of "amens" and a few "hallelujahs" coming from the congregation, particularly from the younger generation. It appeared the preacher hit a home run.

"Gigi, that was a powerful sermon on respect," said Lindsey.

"I wanted you to hear it. It's one of the best on the subject, at least in my opinion. And you would do well to keep it in mind."

"How did you know about it?" Lindsey asked, curious about the whole thing.

"I've got my connections," was all she said.

❀❀❀

"Now that we're in the window of respect," Gigi said, "I think it's time for you to see something that directly concerns you in the here and now. However, I won't take you there without your permission."

"Sounds intriguing. Take me wherever you think I need to go. I completely trust you," said Lindsey.

"Okay. Hold on." And off they flew, back to the present, ending up at a large apartment building.

"I recognize this place." Lindsey said. "This is where Jeff lives. He's got a great little studio apartment. But what are we doing here?"

"You'll see. Let's go in. He invited his mother over for dinner while you've been gone, and they've just finished eating."

"He's a good cook, Gigi. He's cooked for me several times."

"I know."

"He looks good in his barbecue apron, don't you think?" Lindsey said.

"Adorable," Gigi said, "Now let's listen."

Picking up the plates from the table his mother said, "Here, let me help you clean up, Jeff. That's the least I can do for such a delicious meal."

"I'm glad you enjoyed it, Mom. I learned the tricks of the trade from the best cook I know—you."

"Why, thank you, son," she said, pleased with the compliment.

"But cleanup can wait," he said, removing his apron. "We need to talk about something important." With that he guided her to the sofa.

"What is it, Jeff? You sound so serious."

"Well, it is serious," he said. "It's about Lindsey."

"Oh, did you break up?" she perked up.

"Gigi, is that what she's wanting? Why do I need to see this?" Lindsey said. "She hates me. I knew it. I can't deal with having a mother-in-law like that for the rest of my life."

"She doesn't hate you, Lindsey. She's just in an adjustment period. Keep listening."

"No, Mom. We didn't break up. In fact, I'm very much in love with her, and . . ."

"Well, that's very sweet dear," his mother said quickly before he could go further. "It's good to date a person for a few years so you can really know if your love is for real. There are lots of fish in the sea, and you haven't cast your net very far yet." She said, smiling and patting his hand.

"Mother, please listen. I love Lindsey! And I've asked her to marry me. There, now you know," he said, relieved.

"What? You asked her to marry you? And you didn't even discuss it with me first?"

"No, Mom, I didn't because I knew you would try to talk me out of getting married now. I'm ready to take this important step in my life and I hoped with all my heart that you would be happy about it. I don't need your permission, but what I would like is your blessing."

"Okay, when I think the time is right I'll give you my blessing and my full support," she said .

"Mother, the time is right for me . . . now. I love Lindsey and I'm going to marry her, if she'll have me."

"But . . ." his mother started to cry, "that means I'm losing my son, and I guess I'm just not ready for that."

"Now, Lindsey," Gigi said, " watch how Jeff handles this. And while you do remember that how a man treats his mother is pretty close to how he'll treat his future wife."

"I'm watching. Oh, am I watching," Lindsey said, her eyes riveted on the scene.

"Mom, you're not losing your son," Jeff said. "Let me show you something." He went to the cupboard and brought out three candles, each in its own holder. He turned the lights down low and sat back down by his mother's side. He had planned for this moment. He set two of the candles on the coffee table in front of the sofa where he and his mother were sitting, and set the other one aside.

"Mom, this candle is you," he said as he struck a match and lit it. The flame began to flicker and glow. He took the lit candle and touched the flame to the wick of the other one next to it. "And this candle is me. You brought me into the world and lit up my life. You've always been

there for me, Mom, cheering me on and helping me achieve my goals, teaching me how to stand on my own. I'll forever be grateful for that. And I'll always be here for you, too. You never need to worry about that."

"Thank you, son," his mother said. "I need you now, and goodness knows how much I may need you as I grow old."

"You don't need to worry about that," he said squeezing her hand. "And now something wonderful is about to happen for both of us." With a match he lit the other candle and moved it next to the one representing him, with the candle holder touching his. "This candle is Lindsey. She's been shining bright for as long as she's been born, and now she's about to add her light to ours. Notice how much brighter the light is when there are three candles together. That's how your life will be with Lindsey as a daughter-in-law. Brighter than ever. No light will be taken away, only more light will be added."

"More light is always nice," his mother said, a bit reluctantly.

"So you see, Mom, you don't lose a son. You gain a daughter. Of course, this all depends on whether or not she says yes to my proposal."

"That's enough of this conversation," Gigi said. "I just wanted you to see the respectful way he treated his mother on this sensitive issue. I'm impressed with your young man, Lindsey, and I hope you are, too."

"He does have a very tender heart— a great quality," Lindsey said. " But I'm afraid his mother is still not willing to welcome anyone else into their family yet, especially me."

"She just needs a little time to warm up to the idea. Let's move on. There are all kinds of other respect issues you'll be facing when you get married, no matter who the lucky guy is," said Gigi as she took Lindsey's hand and off they went.

❀❀❀

Before Lindsey knew it they were walking down a sidewalk in an urban neighborhood. The yards were neatly kept with mowed lawns and trimmed shrubs. Flowers bloomed in most of the yards. Children were outside playing, riding bicycles, roller blading and having a fun time. It was a pleasant setting.

"Let's walk a bit and look a little deeper into this window of respect," Gigi said. "One big problem that faces newly married couples is what to call the newly acquired parents in-law. Do you call them by their first names, by Mr. and Mrs., by Mom and Dad, or just avoid calling them anything at all. And I gotta tell you 'hey, you' doesn't work. This is a dilemma most folks face, and it has a lot to do with respect."

"I understand," Lindsey said. "I don't know what I'd call Jeff's mother. Right now I call her Mrs. Sloan and she seems happy with that, though she told me once to call her Sarah. I haven't been able to make that transition yet, let alone the 'mother' thing. It'll seem weird to call her anything different, but it'll seem more weird to keep calling her Mrs. Sloan . . . *if* Jeff and I tie the knot."

"Well, whoever you marry you and they are going to have to make a decision on this."

"I know."

"See that couple walking up ahead, Lindsey? Actually it's not a couple, it's a father and a daughter. Let's get close and hear what they're saying. I have an inkling, due to my connections, that you just might be interested."

"Rachel, I can't believe you'll be a married woman this time next week."

"I know, Daddy. I can't either."

"You've always been my little sweetheart."

"I still will be, Daddy."

"No, you're Jared's sweetheart now, but you'll always be my little girl, even if you are a grown-up woman." He put his arm lovingly around her shoulders as they walked on. *"Do you have any concerns you need to talk about?"*

"There is something I'm worried about, Daddy. I don't know what to call Jared's parents after we're married. Jared thinks I should call them the same names he uses, Mom and Dad. But you're my dad, and it feels disloyal for me to call his dad by the same name I call you, and the same for Mom. No one can ever take your place."

They stopped walking and he gently lifted her chin so he could look into her eyes and said, "Rachel, I want you to know something, no one will ever take our place. Your mother and I have discussed this issue and we want you to know that we feel perfectly comfortable about your calling your parents-in-law Mom and Dad. It will show respect to them and to Jared. We give you permission to do that, and it won't diminish our relationship one bit. It won't mean they're taking our place. On the contrary, it will mean you've gained another set of parents who love you, and more love never hurt anybody."

"But, Daddy, it will be so hard, and how do I know if they even want me to?"

"I think it might just be a good idea if you had a conversation with them before the wedding where you ask them if it would be all right to call them Mom and Dad. That shows respect for them. They'll be complimented by your request. It'll show them right off the bat that you're looking forward to being part of their family. I have to tell you, it really tickled us when Jared started calling us Mom and Dad right after your engagement. He's a lot like me. I didn't have any qualms about doing it with my in-laws, but it was an adjustment for your mother. Maybe women are just a little more emotional about things."

"Why, what do you mean, more emotional?" She laughed and hugged him.

Gigi smiled and said, "This dad definitely gets my vote. That's what parents need to do—give their children permission to call their in-laws Mom and Dad. Another thing they need to do is to tell their new in-law children that they would be happy to have them call them Mom and Dad. Or if they prefer being called by their first name—that's fine, too—then they can talk about that. It takes a load off everyone. And it shows respect. Let's say you marry Jeff, how're you going to handle *your* situation, Lindsey?"

"It looks like I would need to ask Jeff's mother if it's okay with her if I call her . . . Gigi, I can't call her Mom, that's the name for my own mother. This is going to be hard."

"Hogwash! You're making it too hard. If you call your mother Mom then why not call his mom Mother?"

"I could do that. Yeah, I could do that."

"Good! And you might want to get your parents on board setting Jeff's mind at ease by letting him know what he can call them. Sometimes people prefer using first names, and that's okay, if that's the decision. In-laws just need to face this head on so nobody gets a burr under their saddle."

Lindsey could see they were still walking with Rachel and her dad. "Does this mean he's got more wisdom to pour out on his daughter, Gigi?"

"Indeed it does. And you'll be wise to drink it in."

"Rachel, I want to share something with you that will help both you and Jared have a good relationship with each other and your in-laws. This is something my father told me and I'm passing it along. He said, 'When you have problems or get upset with your wife don't you come running to me or Mom with your whining or criticism because we'll take your side and always make matters worse. Then ever after we'll look upon your wife with less respect. So keep it to yourselves and work it out. On the other hand, when she does something praiseworthy share it like you're throwing out seeds in rich fertile soil and happy relationships will spring up all over the place.'"

"Daddy, that makes good sense."

"I've followed that counsel and found that it fostered a great deal of trust and respect between my wife and her in-laws. And she's done the same for me. Consequently our in-laws have become very dear to us."

"That was probably easy for you, Daddy, because you and Mom are both such good people. You probably didn't have anything bad to say anyway."

He started to laugh. "You weren't around in those early years of our marriage, Rachel. We had plenty we could have whined about. I was a pretty stubborn guy about some things, and as a result I put your mother to tears more than once. But she was patient and I finally got the picture. It would have been a real problem if she'd run to her daddy about every little thing. And vice-versa. We both had a lot to learn, and learning it without interference was a very good thing."

"But, Daddy, what if, well, you know about Aunt June. Her husband was abusive. I'm sure Jared would never be abusive to me, but maybe she thought the same thing about her husband at first."

"Let me make this point clear. The exception to this rule is abuse. If he ever hits you then he has me to account to. You tell me right away. Abuse is unacceptable. However, if you hit him first, then you're on your own. My dad put it this way, 'What's good for the goose is good for the gander.' You must treat each other with respect."

By now Rachel and her dad were in the neighborhood park and found a bench to sit on. Her father picked a daisy from the bed nearby and gave it to his daughter. She started to pull the petals off saying,

"He loves me, he loves me not . . ."

"Don't play that game, baby girl. Always know he loves you—and so do I."

She pulled one more petal and said, "Okay. He loves me. I'll stop on that."

"Good. Here's another thing to remember. When something wonderful happens in your life be sure to tell your husband first, not us. Otherwise, he may resent us. It's always fun to be the one to receive the news first, whether it's good or bad. It shows respect. Most of the time,

let him be there to hear you tell us. He'll love that. I was appalled when I heard that our neighbor's daughter took a pregnancy test and called the results to her mother before she told her husband. She might as well have smacked him in the face with a wet dishrag."

"Daddy, I would never do that!"

"I hope not. There's something else I hope you will never do. Too many couples do this and it leads to nothing but bitterness. Don't compare Jared with me. If there are things about me you love, and I surely hope there are . . ."

"Oh, Daddy, there are so many things about you I love. I want Jared to be just like you."

"Whoa, sweetheart. You need to keep in mind that it took me nearly fifty years to become who I am, and I'm still working on it. Give Jared time to become who he's going to be. I don't want a son-in-law suffering from the cruel and unusual punishment of comparison with his father-in-law. It reminds me of a little story I heard about a young married couple. The young husband said to his wife, 'You just don't make bread like my mom.' And she got him back with 'And you don't make dough like my dad!' "

"Daddy, that's funny." She laughed.

Chuckling he said, "Yeah, it is. But it's not funny at all if it happens in real life. Give him time to grow and he'll be much more willing to do the same for you. That's showing respect for each other."

"This leads right into another thing I want you to learn from this window of respect," Gigi said, taking Lindsey by the hand. "So, let's get going."

❀❀❀

They ended up in a small apartment in Madison, Wisconsin. Lindsey saw the sign as they whizzed on by.

"This is a college town, Gigi, so I'm guessing this apartment belongs to some students."

"A newly married couple, Alyssa and Eric, a lot like you and Jeff will be—struggling, but happy as two little frogs smooching on their lily pad."

She wasn't far off. Alyssa and Eric were sitting on the sofa, snuggling and talking when their doorbell rang. They both jumped up to answer it.

"Allen residence?" a delivery man asked.

"That's us," said Eric.

"Got a big screen TV for ya. Sign here."

Turning to his wife with a puzzled look on his face he said, "Did you order a TV . . . a big screen TV? We don't have the money for this."

"Of course not. What's going on here?" she asked, equally puzzled.

"It's yours." said the delivery man. "Here's the paper work."

Eric looked it over and saw the name of the purchaser. "Your dad is at it again."

"I'll sign for it, Eric. It's okay," she said.

With some effort the delivery man brought the TV in and set it up.

"Eric. This is fabulous! Dad knew we couldn't afford a TV. Wow, look at this!"

It was impressive, a real state-of-the-art beauty.

"Boy, I wouldn't mind if my Dad bought us one of those," Lindsey said, drooling over the prospects.

"Well, that could happen. He certainly could afford it. Keep listening, Lindsey."

The TV worked perfectly. Without a doubt it was the centerpiece of their small living room. They sat back on the sofa and began watching.

"Here, Eric. I present you with the remote control," she jokingly said.

"No, thanks," he said and got up and went into the bedroom.

Alyssa followed him. "What's the matter, Eric?"

"Nothing."

"Yes, there is. What's going on?"

"It's just that . . . well, I feel bad. Last month it was the new couch, and before that it was the new microwave oven. These were all the things I was hoping to be able to get for you. Alyssa, I want to be the provider in our family, not your father," he said.

"But Daddy's only trying to help us."

"Yes, I know. But I was wanting to surprise you on your birthday. I put a little TV on lay-a-way and have been paying on it a little at a time. But that one's insignificant compared to what your Dad just had delivered. He makes me feel worthless." Eric was hurt; there was no question about it.

Alyssa put her arms around him, hugged him tenderly and said, "Eric, I don't know what to say. I'm very touched that you were going to surprise me. We'll send this one back."

"No. The surprise is ruined now. I know your dad means well, it's just hard for me." He kissed her on the cheek and said. "I've got to study now."

"Gigi, this is a problem. Can't he see that all her dad wants to do is help them? Can't he just accept the help and be grateful?" Lindsey said.

"Try to see it from his position. Put yourself in his shoes—that's always a good idea in marriage no matter what the problem is—and you'll see a different view. A man wants to be the provider of the good things for his wife and family. It isn't a matter of gratitude, it's a matter of fulfilling his job, and a wife needs to pay attention to it."

"Isn't that the same thing that motivates her dad to keep on providing for his little girl?" Lindsey asked.

"I think you've nailed it; but his season for that has passed. Eric decided it was time to do something about it, so he went straight to the source. Let's look in at his father-in-law's house a few days later."

"Hi, Dad," said Eric as he entered the house.

"What's up, Eric? You said you needed to talk to me and it sounded serious. Is everything okay?" his father-in-law asked.

"We're fine. I just need to talk to you about something that's bugging me." He shoved his hands in his pockets and went for it. "Dad, I really appreciate all the kind things you do for us, but you need to know what it's doing to me. I want to be the one to provide Alyssa with these nice things, and it's true I can't do it quite the way you can,

but I want to. And when I graduate next fall I'll be able to do it even better. But, well, I'm asking you to stop showering us with so many expensive gifts. We're okay struggling together to make our life happen in our own way," he said.

"Why, Eric, I had no idea," he said apologetically.

"I know you didn't, Dad. I hope you understand. We both love you and Mom and wouldn't want to hurt your feelings for anything."

"It's okay, Eric. I'll be much more judicious in my gift giving from now on. Mother warned me I might be getting my nose in where it shouldn't be. Guess I should've listened to her. Well, I'm listening to you now, son. Please forgive me. I have confidence that you'll be a fine provider for your family. If I can ever be of help please let me know."

"Thanks, Dad," he said and they embraced.

"What an understanding father-in-law," Lindsey said.

"Yes, and what a brave son-in-law," Gigi replied. "They both showed great respect for each other in resolving this problem. When parents allow their grown children to make their own lives happen, just like we talked about in the boundaries window, then they develop into responsible people, appreciating the good things they've worked hard to get."

"What if the father still keeps on giving things? What then?"

"That would be rare, but if it did happen, it's a good idea to simply say thank you and not let it ruin your relationship. And if you don't like the stuff, well, then get acquainted with eBay.

❀❀❀

"One last thing regarding respect, Lindsey. This mostly has to do with mothers and daughters-in-law. Too many times when a mother calls her son's home she by-passes her daughter-in-law. Let's look in on a conversation to see a good way to handle this situation.

"Hello, Suzanne. How are you doing?"

"Oh, Hi, Mom. Great, and how about you?"

"I'm fine, too. Dad and I were wondering if you, Wayne and the kids could come for dinner this Sunday. We're in the mood for some grandchildren hugs."

"They'll love it . . . we all will. And I'm in the mood for some of your good cooking."

"Good. Will 3:00 work for you?"

"Perfect," Suzanne said.

"Is Wayne home? I'd like to say Hi to him and let him know about Sunday, too."

"I'll get him for you."

"Now that's showing respect," Gigi said. "Too many times mothers ask for their sons instead of talking with their daughters-in-law about things. It's hurtful to the daughter-in-law. Also, sad to say, too many sons forget to tell their wives about the conversation and an invitation can go unheeded."

"Not showing up could put a real damper on an in-law relationship," Lindsey said.

"Absolutely.

"In summary of this window of respect, let me remind you of these Pertinent Points: be your in-laws' friend, not their boss or their slave, and honor their right to make their own choices without being offended.

"Time to move on. We have another important window to open."

Chapter Eight
Window of Privacy

*I*n no time at all they were standing on an empty lot, next to a rather large house. Cows were grazing in a pasture only a few yards away near a big red barn with a rooster weather vane on top. No question about it, they were on a farm. Out of the house came the farmer wearing blue overalls and his aproned wife in a pretty print dress. Close behind came a young couple, the father carrying their baby.

"Billy, this is the property we promised you when you had your first child. You and your wife can build your house right here next to ours."

"Gigi, even I can see this is an in-law problem in the making," Lindsey observed.

"You mean you wouldn't like to live right next door to your mother-in-law?"

"*I'm* concerned about living in the same city," she said being out-right honest.

"Well, let's see how this plays out."

"What is this window anyway?" Lindsey asked.

"I'm going to let you guess as we move along."

"Okay, I'm game."

"Good. I'm not squandering any time here. Let's get right to the heart of it," she said. "The whole family and the neighbors worked hard and that house was up in no time at all. You see, not only is Billy's dad a farmer, he's a builder. His building skills actually pay more bills than the farming, but he does love farming on the side."

Suddenly they were standing by the finished house. "Gigi, I wish we could build a house this fast. It's beautiful."

"They did a nice job and the little family is all settled in. Now watch what happens, Lindsey."

"Oh, Billy, I do love our new home," said the young mother as she stood at the bay window burping her baby on her shoulder.

"Gracie, this is a dream come true."

"Did he call her Gracie? Gigi, is this you?" Lindsey asked a bit shocked.

"Well, I was young once, you know. I know all about this window. This is where I learned so much about being an in-law."

"Gigi, Billy's a handsome dude—you did good!"

"He was my man! And we were so in love. Besides that, his dad taught him well and he was a fine, respectable builder himself."

"And you were so pretty."

"Thank you kindly, but that was a long time ago," Gigi said with a chuckle.

"I think you still are, just a deeper kind of pretty."

"Yeah, the deep wrinkles kind."

"Stop it," Lindsey said. "And look at that baby, she's so adorable."

"He. But cute enough to be a girl."

"Did you have other children?"

"Twin girls next, and four babies after that. All in this house."

"Wow. How did you do it, Gigi?"

"It wasn't easy, but who said life was supposed to be easy? We wouldn't be worth a lick if it was all a bed of roses. Still, certain things happen that are like little bouquets along the way, and that makes all the difference. Watch."

The scene changed to a few years later, and they were in the young couple's bedroom. Draped over the end of the bed was a colorful patchwork quilt. Gracie was lying in bed with a baby in each arm. Billy walked over to the bed, reached down and took one of the babies in his arms.

"The good Lord has double blessed us, Gracie. How are you feeling?"

"Better. It was a bit of a task bringing these two little angels into the world, but I'm getting stronger every day."

Just then there was a knock on the front door. A woman opened the door slightly and said, "Hello. It's Mom. May I come in?"

Billy went to the open bedroom door and called out, "We're in the bedroom, Mom. Come on back."

A little blond-haired boy was at her side. "What have you got there, Mom?" Billy asked.

"Timmy and I have been busy. We brought you a pot of your favorite beef stew and . . ." She looked down at the little boy, nodding to give him a cue.

"Me an' Grammy cooked up some muffins!" he shouted handing up a basket full to his daddy.

He awkwardly took them with one hand while balancing the baby in the other arm. "Thanks, Timmy," he said. "They smell good."

"They are good. I ate some already," the little boy said, grinning.

With a look of nostalgia on her face, Gigi said, "My mother-in-law was remarkable. Let me point out a few things to you. She knew how to be there when I needed her and gone when I didn't. When we moved our things into this house she and Billy's dad were right there to help, and the nice thing was neither of them put things in place without asking us where we wanted them. Since that day she never entered without knocking first, and we showed them the same respect. She was very conscious of our . . ." She waited for Lindsey to fill in the blank.

"Privacy," Lindsey said. "So this is the window of privacy!"

"You're so smart I'd swear you were related to me." Then barely whispered, "but you're not . . . yet."

"What did you say?" Lindsey couldn't quite hear what she had said, since her voice had trailed off in a whisper at the end.

"Nothing. Now watch this scene. After we lived there a few years, a new couple moved in down the road. Nellie and Clyde were their names. We liked those names so much we named our horses after them, course we never told them. Well, anyway they had a similar situation with his folks living close by. Many were the days she'd come crying to me. I wanted to go right over and give her mother-in-law 'what for,' but it wasn't my business, so I just listened. That seemed to help her calm down."

"What did she tell you?" Lindsey asked, more than a little curious.

"Same as us, his folks helped them build their house on his dad's property. She said there was trouble from day one even in the designing phase. Nellie wanted a bay window like we had, and her mother-in-law said, 'No, takes too much heat out of the house.' She wanted a separate dining room and the response was, 'Waste of space. I never had one and got along just fine. Eat in the kitchen like most folks out here do.' Her mother-in-law even chose the paint and carpet colors. And Nellie just rolled over and took it, hating her all the while."

"Gigi, that's sad."

"You ain't heard nothing yet. When they moved in, the in-laws insisted on having their own set of keys to the house, so they could come and go at will whether Clyde and Nellie were there or not. And do you think they had the courtesy to knock when they came calling? No, just burst right in unannounced. One evening after the kids were in bed asleep Nellie said she and Clyde were making spontaneous whoopie on the sofa and in walks his mother and catches them . . ."

"Gigi!"

"Hey, I'm just telling it like she said."

"This is awful."

"Making whoopie's not awful," Gigi said.

"I mean bursting in like that. Didn't they do anything about it? Didn't Clyde say anything to his parents?"

"Nope. He was a chicken heart. It just got worse, to the point that they all just pretty much couldn't stand one another. It was a pitiful thing, and so unnecessary. By comparison I felt like I was living in paradise and she was living in, well, you know where."

"Privacy is very important." Lindsey said. "They all needed to take a look through your boundaries window. I think a few good boundaries could have set things right."

"I wish they could have. After a few years Clyde and Nellie just up and moved as far away as they could get, and rumor has it they had very little to do with his parents ever again. Tragic. So much loving was missed out on. I was a lucky girl to have married into a family that respected our privacy and yet were ever so full of caring and love."

"That's the kind of relationship I'm hoping for, Gigi. But what about your parents, did your husband get along with them?"

"I had good parents, though they weren't of the same nature as Billy's. They lived in the next county so we didn't see them as much. To tell the truth I felt closer to Billy's mother than I did my own. But my folks were good people, raised me to be honest and upright. Billy's such an easy-going guy that it's hard to get his dander up, but I do remember an incident that taught us both a good lesson. Here it comes. Watch and you'll see. My folks had come visiting for the day. It was during a particularly difficult time, the building industry was taking a recess and we were just squeaking by. As they were about to leave, my father did something that totally surprised us."

"Billy and Gracie," her father said, "We've noticed since being here that you could sure use a new table and chairs for the kitchen. Yours is getting a little shabby what with all the kids wear and tear on it, so we want to give you some money to buy a new set."

"He wrote a check for a hundred dollars and gave it to us," said Gigi. "That was a fair piece of the pie in those days. Billy and I were pretty much speechless. We thanked them, hugged them and they left."

"So what's the problem? Sounds like they did a very kind thing."

"Well, it was kind. Only thing was, it wasn't the kind of kind we were in need of. Listen."

"Gracie, this is like a gift from heaven," Billy said. "Haven't we been praying for some help to pay the mortgage this month, and well it looks like the good Lord just answered us."

"Oh, I know, Billy, it sure does. But what will Mom and Dad say when they find out we didn't use the money to buy the new table and chairs? They're going to be real upset."

"Better they be upset than we lose our credit rating with the bank, or worse yet, our house," he said.

"Remember when we gave your sister that silver tray for her wedding?" Gracie said. "We had saved up for that and thought it was something she'd cherish for years to come. And when we found out she traded it in for some fancy bed sheets we were downright disgusted at her."

"I remember, and that was pretty silly of us. After all, we gave it to her, and once it's hers she can do what she darn well pleases. Gifts hadn't ought to come tethered to restrictions."

"That's right, but I don't want to hurt my parents. They'll come by in a couple of weeks and are going to be looking for the new table."

"I have an idea, Gracie. Let's be right up front with them. Let's write them a thank you note and tell them the whole thing straight out."

Gigi was reminiscing. "We sat down at our 'shabby' kitchen table with pen and paper and started composing. Look there, Billy's reading the note back to make sure it sounds good."

"Dear Mom and Dad,
We want to thank you for the $100 you gave us. You didn't know this, but we had been praying hard for a way to pay our mortgage since business has been so bad lately. We didn't want to tell anybody about our struggle, except in our prayers. It was

*like God touched your hearts and answered our prayers through
you. We'll find a way to get a new table and chairs later, but in
the meantime we thank you for saving our house.
We love you, Gracie and Billy*

"How'd they take it?" Lindsey asked.

"They called us right up after they got the note and said
they were happy to be God's instruments in answering our
prayers, and we were not to worry about getting the table
and chairs. We were mighty relieved. We found that being
forthright with your loved ones is the winning way to go."

"I'm beginning to get the picture," Lindsey said.

"Good, because once you give a gift to someone it's a
private matter what they do with it after that. If your intent
in giving it is to make them happy, then whatever makes them
happy regarding it ought to be enough. The only exceptions
are tuition and heirlooms. And that's that." She dusted her
hands together like she was through with that subject.

"Do we have another window to explore?"

"Not quite yet. There's another matter regarding privacy
I want to discuss with you. Some people pour out their
problems to their kids as if they were the family clergyman.
Let me show you what I mean."

In the next breath they were in a coffee shop. "We'll just
slide in right next to Maggie and her daughter Carly and get

an ear full while they eat their club sandwiches," she said. And they did.

"Thanks for taking me to lunch, Mom. This is a real treat," Carly said.

"Boy, has she got that wrong," Gigi said, spilling the beans prematurely.

"I wanted to have you alone, Carly, so we could talk. I'm so upset at your father. Ever since our separation I just keep finding out more and more slimy little tidbits about him. I am so hurt by what he has done to dishonor me and our family. Just when I was starting to think I might someday get over the terrible hurt of his affair, and maybe even forgive him, this happens. His little 'paramour' calls the house asking if he's there. Do you know what this is doing to me, Carly? I can just picture him kissing her, touching her. Can you even imagine the pictures that are going on in my head? It's just awful."

"Oh, Mom. I'm so sorry," she said taking her mother's hand and patting it like a mother would a child.

"This whole thing is such a mess," the mother said reaching in her purse for a tissue. "I just don't know what I'm going to do. How could your father do this to me?" The tears were coming. "I was so stupid to believe him last year when he said he was working late. You just can't believe men, Carly. He was messing around then and I didn't even know it— climbing in bed with heaven only knows who. I just can't take it."

"Please don't cry, Mom. Things will work out somehow."

That kind of dialogue went on for another thirty minutes. It was a pathetic situation.

"Gigi, it seems like she shouldn't be saying all this to her daughter," Lindsey said, feeling sorry for the daughter.

"Exactly! It's not fair to the daughter for more reasons than one. Here's the indirect effect this mother-in-law is about to have on her son-in-law. Let's go to Carly's house that night."

They were in bed and Carly's husband Nick started to put his arm around her.

"I'm not in the mood, Nick."

"What's the matter?" he said moving closer.

"Please. Men just have one thing on their minds, and you're no exception," she said turning away from him.

"What'd I do?"

"I don't want to talk about it. G'night."

"Did you see that, Lindsey? Her mother just plain and simple crawled in bed between them and pulled in Carly's father with all of his concubines, figuratively speaking, but nonetheless they're there. She set the stage for Carly to doubt her own husband. And besides that, she's weighed her down like a mobster putting cement blocks on a victim he's about to toss in the river. A mother should never lay her problems on her child like that, no matter the age of the child. It's too heavy a burden. It will always take a toll on the child's marriage."

"So what do you do if a parent starts to dump on you like this?"

"Just look her in the eye and say, 'Mom, I know this is painful for you, but this is not something I want you to be telling me. I'd be happy to help you find a good therapist, but it can't be me. You'll always have my love, and I will be here for you in every other way, but I can't be your therapist. Mom, I can't handle the intimate struggles between you and Dad. Good or bad he's still my father.'

"This is an extreme case, but it's a sample of how inappropriate it is to talk about intimate, private matters with your children. And that works both ways. Don't be telling private details to your parents or in-laws. It'll come back to bite your marriage. It's a betrayal of trust."

"Are there any intimate things you *can* share with your parents?" Lindsey asked.

"Yes, but only in a general way, and that goes for both sides. Let's look in on another mother and her daughter-in-law to see how that works."

❀❀❀

There they were, hanging out in someone's house again. The mother and her daughter-in-law were making cookies, and talking away like crazy. It was obvious they had a close relationship.

"Hannah," the mother-in-law said, "I've gotta tell you about this class I went to last week. It was called 'How to Spark up Your Marriage.'"

"*Are you and Dad having marital problems?*" *Hannah asked with a bit of alarm in her voice.*

"*Goodness no! I just thought the class might be kinda fun. I think all marriages could use a little sparkin' up. Well, the instructor said it can be a lot of fun if you spice up your sleep wear with some tempting intimate apparel. Hannah, I have to admit, I have no spicy intimate apparel and I'm not sure I'd even know what to get or where to get it.*"

Putting down a tray of steaming hot cookies she had just taken out of the oven, Hannah removed her oven mitts and said with an air of confidence, "*You have come to the right source. Follow me, Mom.*"

She wiped her hands on the towel and obeyed. They went into the master bedroom, shut the door, and went to the walk-in closet. Hannah turned the light on and gestured to one corner of the closet.

"*Here's what the instructor was talking about,*" *Hannah said as she showed her mother-in-law her collection of lovely satin and lace nighties.* "*Pick one, Mom. You're my size. No need to even buy one. Believe me, it won't get much wear. I don't know what it is about these outfits but they come off faster than . . . well, you get the idea.*"

"*Oh, my! You wear these every night?*"

"*No. I wear my comfy pajamas most of the time,*" *Hannah said.* "*I save these for special occasions.*"

"*What's a special occasion?*"

"*Birthdays, anniversaries, a special date night, you name it. Once I wore this one to celebrate the first time Tony changed our baby's dirty diaper. He's been more willing ever since. You name it, I celebrate it with one of these. And I enjoy the celebration as much as he does. It's fun to look extra pretty and a little sexy. Go ahead. Choose one.*"

"*You do this for Tony?*"

"I love makin' my man happy," Hannah said. *"Go ahead, Mom. Choose one."*

"Your father-in-law will have a heart attack."

"Then he'll go out of this world with a smile on his face. Mom, he won't have a heart attack, he'll love it."

"I like this one," her mother-in-law said, pointing to a black satin gown.

"Oooo. Black satin is a good choice," Hannah said. *"He's gonna eat you up in this."*

"He's gonna turn red and run."

"Bet he doesn't," she said as she took it off the hanger and put it in a bag. *"Here, Mom. It's yours to keep. Enjoy it."*

"Thank you, I think."

Back to the kitchen they went. "Tonight tell him you've got a special treat for him," Hannah said. *"Fix up a plate of these cookies, then sneak away and put on the surprise and deliver the cookies to him wearing it."*

"Did she do it, Gigi?" Lindsey asked, curious beyond words.

"Indeed she did. Just as they planned."

"Did he turn red and run?"

"Nope," said Gigi. "He turned red, but he didn't run. On the contrary. The brief entry in her journal said they had 'a very entertaining evening.'"

"I'll bet they did," said Lindsey.

"Next morning Hannah called her to see how things went."

"Did you wear it, Mom?" Hannah asked.

"Just like you said."

"What happened?"

"None of your business."

Hannah laughed. "It worked, didn't it?"

"I'll just say this, our marriage has definitely been sparked. And that's all I'm saying. The rest is private. Oh, one more thing. Thanks!" she said with a smile in her voice. "So, how's the baby?"

"You see, Lindsey, you can share a few things, but not the details. It's the details that cause the problem. So my Pertinent Point here is: keep your nose out of their private business and theirs out of yours."

"This was a good window, Gigi. I can't wait to see where we go next."

Chapter Nine
Window of Compassion

*T*hey were walking along a path beside a shimmering lake, surrounded by mountains and large pines. Squirrels scurried as they approached. The songs of birds filled the air as rays of sunlight filtered through the pine branches. The scene was peaceful and beautiful.

"This seems like a good place to open another window," Gigi said.

"Oh, I wish I had a window that opened up to this view every day," Lindsey said, breathing in the fresh clean air. There was not a cloud in the sky. It was a perfect summer day. They came upon a middle-aged couple sitting on the raised bank of the lake. Several yards away was a lovely little cabin nestled in the woods. The husband was nonchalantly tossing pebbles into the water as he and his wife talked.

"It was nice of your boss to let us use his cabin for the weekend," the wife said.

"He understands what we're going through and thought it would be a nice break for us," he responded.

"And it is!" she said with a sudden exuberance. *"It's so peaceful up here."*

"Marilyn, I really appreciate you," the husband said as he took her hand in his.

"I know you do, Frank. This is a hard time for you, for all of us," she said, and by the look on her face it was obvious she felt deep love for him. *"Your father needs us and we're going to be there for him."*

"What's going on here, Gigi? What's happening to his father?"

"He's been ill with Parkinson's for several years. Frank's mother, who had taken good care of him, passed away unexpectedly from a heart attack last year, leaving the responsibility of his care to their children. Frank has a younger brother who lives clear across the country from them. Both he and his wife work full time and still have a couple of kids at home. They haven't been able to help out much. So Frank and Marilyn moved their father in with them. Frank is still working, but Marilyn retired from her job early so she could be there to care for him. Their daughter helps out on some weekends to give them a break . . . like this weekend, a break they badly needed."

"Frank's lucky he has a wife like Marilyn, who's willing to help," Lindsey said as they watched them there by the lake.

"True. But you need to understand that this is not easy for Marilyn. Listen."

"Frank, sometimes I'm so sad about this whole situation. Mostly I'm sad about your father but I'm ashamed to say that many times I feel more sorry for myself than for him."

"Oh, Marilyn, don't be ashamed. You're an amazing woman. Sometimes when I'm at work thinking about you I feel like I married an angel."

"I'm not an angel. Too often I think about what my plans were before your mother passed away. I was going to retire early so you and I could enjoy our life and have more fun, and so I could spend more time with our grandchildren—not so I could do full-time care of your father. At times I resent it. Other times I wonder if I have the physical strength to do it. I thought I could, but now I'm not sure."

"It's okay to resent it, honey. Sometimes I do, too. And yet I love Dad and want us to be there for him, and I couldn't do this without you."

"I love him, too. He's a good man and he certainly didn't ask for this," Marilyn said.

"Looks like this whole situation put a roadblock in Marilyn's plans," Lindsey said. "That would be so difficult."

"Life has a way of doing that to us," Gigi said, "and how we handle it turns us into who we really are. We can be transformed by the troubles that come into our lives.[18] It's been said that 'He who has no cross will have no crown.' Life is a test, and Marilyn is busy trying to pass the test right now, and being a devoted daughter-in-law is part of the deal. You might say she's in the act of earning her crown."

"So this window is about caring," Lindsey said, thinking she'd hit the target.

"Close. I call it the window of compassion. Compassion goes a step beyond caring; it engages your full heart and allows you to put yourself in the other person's place. By doing so you can see the needs beyond the perfunctory duties. That's when you find joy in the service. But it's still very hard. And that's what Marilyn is dealing with."

"Gigi, how do you graduate from giving care to giving compassion?" She wanted to know because she was beginning to realize that it was possible for something like this to happen in her future. She found herself wondering what might lie ahead with her own parents or in-laws.

"It's a process that can be endured best with a lot of prayer," Gigi said. "You can outright ask God for a compassionate heart. And He's going to be eager to help you have it because that's exactly what He wants. Remember, He's the one who said, 'Love one another as I have loved you.' There's no one who knows how to show compassion better than He does.

"Another thing you can do," Gigi said, "is simply keep saying to yourself, 'What if this were me? What would I want done?' That brings to mind something else Jesus said, 'Therefore all things whatsoever ye would that men should do to you, do ye even so to them.'[19] Do that and it'll put your graduation cap on real fast."

Lindsey was beginning to think Gigi had the very pages of the Bible imbedded in her head, and she was being blessed because of it.

"Lindsey, I remember when my own mother was nearing the end of her days. When she could no longer take care of herself we moved her into our home. My dear husband always loved my mother, and she him. He would playfully tease her and put a little life into her living, and I could tell she ate it up. I'm so grateful for all the help he gave me through her final two years. People need to understand that when a husband loves his wife's mother, he endears himself to his wife even more. And, of course, it works both ways."

"None of us know what's ahead, do we?" Lindsey said in somber thought.

"No, and it's good we don't. Now here's a big side benefit to it all. Folks like Frank and Marilyn are setting a mighty secure stage for their future. You see, their children are eye witnesses of how you show love to your parents and in-laws, no matter what happens. Not a bad insurance policy, I'd say. But there's another side to compassion that's opening up in Frank's mind right now."

Their attention switched back to the couple.

"Marilyn, I didn't realize how hard this was on you. Oh, I knew it was hard, but I didn't fully understand what you were going through. We've got to figure out what we can do to make this work out better," Frank said thoughtfully.

"It was on this weekend away," Gigi said, "that they came up with a plan that took some of the load off of Marilyn. When he started seeing things through *her* eyes his mind got into gear like never before. A good dose of compassion from your mate can go a long way in helping you have compassion for his parents."

"What'd they do?"

"They cashed in some stocks and hired someone to come in to relieve Marilyn two days a week. It made a big difference. She still carried much of the load, but with this break she felt a new surge of energy for the task."

"So maybe he did a little of that 'do unto others' thing regarding his wife," Lindsey said.

"I'd say so," Gigi said. "It was as though he had taken a good look through the window of a listening heart."

"But what if they hadn't had any stocks to cash in? What then?"

"Same game, even if it means working out a schedule with your boss so you can be home more, maybe working a ten-hour day four days a week and spending the extra day at home. There's always a way to find a solution that lightens another's load."

"Or maybe rent a room to a college student," Lindsey said, "in exchange for a certain number of hours of care for the father. I know a student who did that and it worked," Lindsey said.

"Like they say, where there's a will there's a way."

❀❀❀

Now I want to show you another application of compassion. It happened to a woman named Laura. She was struggling with a couple of in-law issues. Her husband's parents were so pleased when she and Blake had a baby. You see, when Blake and Laura got married she was forty and nearly out of the childbearing stage. Laura was afraid her well was running dry and dared not wait to have a baby. Blake, a couple of years younger, was willing, so when that little testing strip popped up with "You're pregnant," they were ecstatic, and so were their parents, especially Blake's since he was their only hope for a grandchild. When their baby girl was born Blake's parents showered her with gifts and came to see her at the drop of a hat, which wasn't difficult because they lived in a nearby city."

"What about Laura's parents?" Lindsey said.

"They were happy for Laura, but rarely came to visit and seemed somewhat aloof, which hurt her more than she cared to admit. Her parents had divorced and each had new spouses and stepchildren to deal with, and they all lived further away. So while Blake's parents were playing Santa Claus on a weekly basis, Laura's parents hadn't even climbed on the sleigh. His parents came by a little too often for her liking. She was beginning to resent them for caring too much, and at the same time resenting her own parents for not caring enough. She was confused. One day while driving home from work she turned on the radio."

"Today, folks," said the radio host, "we're talking about a little purple monster that can climb on your back and mercilessly hack away at your head, if you let him, and wreak all kinds of havoc in your relationships. And for you who have just tuned in, his name is . . . Drum roll, please." On came the drum roll. "Tuh duh! Resentment!"

"Gigi, that's you again! I know that's your voice!" Lindsey said more convinced than ever.

"You're going to miss the point here if you keep rattling on. Shhhh."

"We have a caller," announced the host. "Hello, Pam."

"Oh, thank goodness! I finally got through to you," the caller said.

"I'm mighty glad you did. Now what's on your mind?"

"I've been trying to have a baby for the past six years. We've tried everything and nothing has helped. Then my younger brother gets married and wham! just like that my sister-in-law is pregnant. My mother's so happy you'd think she won the lottery. This will be their first grandchild. And all I can do is cry. I resent that this has happened to them and not me. I should be happy for my brother and sister-in-law, but I'm not."

"What's your question for me?"

"How do I deal with this?" said the caller. "What can I do to overcome the resentment I'm feeling toward my sister-in-law . . . and my mother?"

"There's another word closely associated with resentment and in this case it seems to be rising to the top. Plain and simple, you're jealous."

"Okay, I'll admit that. I'm jealous that she's having the baby instead of me."

"Now let's get serious," the radio host said, *"What kind of person are you, really?"*

"What do you mean? I'm a good person," said the caller.

"At least you're an honest person, you admitted you were jealous. Are you a person who respects others?"

"I think so."

"Are you a person who loves her family?"

"Of course, I am," the caller said.

"So what does that mean?"

"What do you mean, what does it mean? It means I love them and I wouldn't want anything terrible to happen to any of them."

"How about something good happening to them?"

There was a pause and then the caller said, *"Oh, no! I see what you mean."*

"Love means rejoicing in the good that happens in their lives not just being glad that bad things didn't. If you are a person who loves and cares about others, can you accept and rejoice when good things happen to them?"

"I was happy when my brother got married, and even when he got promoted at work. So why can't I be happy over this?"

"None of the other things were things you didn't already have. Are you going to go through your life resenting people who get things that you want but can't have? When your neighbors get the new car you want but can't afford, are you going to resent them? When your best friend buys a home bigger than yours, are you going to resent her for that? Life can be terribly miserable when you go through it resenting

the good things that happen to others. You have to decide what kind of a person you're going to be."

"I want to be a kind, loving person," the caller said. "And I thought I was, but I can see I've got to change or I'm going to end up a miserable mess."

"So what can you do right now to find joy in the birth of your brother and sister-in-law's baby? Think about it a minute and I'll get right back to you after the break."

After a few commercials she was back on, and Lindsey was captivated.

"So, Pam, have you thought of how you can find happiness in the birth of this new baby?" the radio host asked.

"Okay. I've got an idea. I could call up my sister-in-law right now and thank her for bringing my very first niece or nephew into the world. I can get excited about being an aunt!"

"Excellent! Yes, you can."

"And I could give her a baby shower and even ask Mom if she'd like to help. I'm good at giving parties, and we could have a humdinger for her."

"Great idea," said the host. "Congratulations! You're beginning to put yourself in her shoes. That's love."

"Yeah, and the shoes feel real good. Thank you!"

Gigi was grinning from ear to ear. "I love it when goodness rises to the top," she said. "Now remember Laura? She was listening to all of this on her car radio. After the caller hung up Laura quickly turned off the radio and right out loud said to herself, 'What kind of person am I?' It made her think. She decided to be grateful for the love Blake's parents showed to their baby. And in the process she discovered that by doing so she would be showing compassion to Blake also; these were his parents, after all, and he loved them. To do otherwise could drive a wedge between him and them, and also between her daughter and her grandparents or even worse, between her and Blake. That would be a terrible outcome for all of them."

"But what about *her* parents?" Lindsey asked.

"She took a serious look at her own parents' situation, put herself in their shoes and realized that they were dealing with a full plate already. She would accept their love on their terms. She made the conscious decision to be a compassionate person. You see, a truly compassionate heart is the antidote for resentment."

"That's profound, Gigi."

"Thanks. And you're a smart student," Gigi said, smiling.

❀❀❀

"Since we're talking about babies," Gigi said, "I'm reminded of another example of compassion between two sisters-in-law, Bailey and Shari. Bailey's baby girl was five months old and Shari's little boy was only two months. Since they lived hundreds of miles apart they hadn't seen each other's babies yet. A family wedding brought them all together. Shari's baby was not doing well on his mother's milk and he was losing weight, and she and her husband were very concerned. Bailey's five-month-old baby girl, on the other hand, was the picture of health with thighs twice the size of Shari's baby's skinny little ones. This is a perfect set-up for resentment and jealously, if they allow it. Listen to their conversation."

"Bailey, I'm so worried about my baby. He keeps losing weight and he can't afford to lose any more. He's so tiny already. The doctor said to keep nursing and be patient, but this isn't a good sign." Putting aside all self-interest and ego, she said, *"What is it that keeps your baby so healthy?"*

"She's drinking pure cream!" Bailey said. *"My milk is so rich it's disgusting. And I have far more than my baby can handle. I always pump and throw away the extra. I would love to share it with you for Bobby, if that's okay."*

"I would love it! I'll nurse him with mine and then top it off with yours."

"And that's exactly what they did for the five days they were together," Gigi said. "Little Bobby drank that cream like it was going out of style, which indeed it was in five more days. He gained two ounces a day! That's ten ounces that little guy gained while they were there. It gave him the jump start he needed. Several days after returning home Shari called her sister-in-law."

"Bailey, I don't know how I can ever thank you enough. Bobby is doing so well. Now he's drinking my milk much better and keeps gaining as he should. Thank you so much."

"My pleasure. To think that I could help you and your baby is one of the happiest things that could happen to me. I was fortunate to have rich milk and I count it a blessing to have been able to share it with you."

"I love it when in-laws work together, showing compassion to each other. This is a case where there was no jealousy, just compassion. And that's how it should be. After all, we're all in this world together and when things get tough it's mighty nice to have compassionate in-laws around," Gigi said. "I think we all need to loan a little milk now and then, so to speak."

❋❋❋

"I saw another evidence of in-law compassion a couple of years ago." Lindsey was right in the groove with Gigi. "It was when my cousin's wife, Cindy, was suffering from a terrible case of postpartum depression, and it wasn't just the 'baby blues.' It hit her after their fourth child was born, when he was about three months old. She was a few hundred miles away from the nearest relative. Mom told me Cindy's friends had helped her a lot by bringing in some meals and helping take care of the kids, but no one really knew the depth of her depression. Her own mother was too ill to help, so she didn' tell her what was going on. No one really knew, apparently not even her husband understood the extent of it, until that one day when my Aunt Samantha, her mother-in-law, called to check on her."

"Yes. They had developed a close relationship through the years, and she was genuinely concerned. Let's look in on that call," Gigi said. Lindsey was eager to see what had really happened. They were in the hotel room where her Aunt Samantha was making the call.

"I know you haven't been feeling well, Cindy. How are you doing now? We've been gone on this trip for the past ten days and are getting ready to return home. I was thinking about you and thought I'd call and check," Samantha explained.

"Oh, Mom," Cindy broke into tears. "I can't even get out of bed. I don't know what's wrong with me."

"Where's Rick?"

"He's at work. He can't afford to miss any more days," Cindy was sobbing out the answers.

"What about the children?"

"We couldn't find anyone to help today. They're running all over the house. I can't get out of my bed. It's like I don't even care what happens to them. This is not like me. What's the matter with me!"

"Where's the baby?"

"Asleep next to me. Poor thing, having me for a mother. I don't think I've slept for days. I can't concentrate, my head is pounding. Everything is going wrong."

"We're in Chicago getting ready to leave, but I won't fly home. I'll reroute my ticket and I'll be there to help you in a few hours," Samantha said.

"Oh, thank you, Mom."

"Hang in there, dear. I'm coming and will stay 'til we get things worked out. Bye for now."

Samantha turned to her husband and said, "Cindy's not doing well at all. It sounds like postpartum depression, and it keeps getting worse. She can't even get out of bed and has lost all sense of caring. This is critical. I've got to go help her."

"Of course you do. I'll take care of things at home while you're gone. Get her to a doctor as soon as you can," he said.

"I will. Could you call Shirley when you get home and tell her I can't help with the club luncheon after all? She'll understand."

They made the new reservation, packed up and left in a rush to catch their separate flights. A few hours later Samantha was in San Diego taking a cab to Cindy and Rick's home. She rushed into the house. The children were excited to see their grandmother. She hugged them and went straight to the bedroom, took Cindy in her arms and held her for a few minutes while she cried uncontrollably. Samantha just held her, and in a soothing voice kept saying, "It's okay, dear, it's okay."

"Do you see that teardrop trickling down your aunt's cheek?" Gigi said. "Her heart is aching for Cindy. Reminds me of the words of that old English poet Byron, 'The dew of compassion is a tear.' When someone you love is suffering it's hard to hold back the tears."

There was no question about it, Gigi had a bona fide soft side, and Lindsey was the witness.

"When the tears subsided," Gigi said, "Cindy thanked Samantha over and over."

Then Lindsey and Gigi watched as this loving mother-in-law shifted into high gear. She changed the baby and while Cindy nursed him she went to the kitchen where the table was covered with peanut butter and honey and spilled milk. Samantha enlisted the help of the two oldest children and straightened up the house. She was busy as a freeway at rush hour—putting in a batch of laundry, taking care of the baby, breaking up kid quarrels, checking on the food situation, answering the phone and a dozen other things. It made Lindsey's head spin just witnessing it all. About six o'clock Rick came home.

"Oh, Mom! Thank you for coming!" He hugged her immediately. "I called to check on Cindy and she said you were on your way. I can't tell you what a relief this is. I don't know what to do."

She hugged him back and then gave him a list. "After you spend a few minutes with your wife, would you go get these groceries? And take a couple of the kids with you. While you're gone I'll get some dinner started."

"Sounds good. Mom, I've been so worried. I took her to the doctor last week and he said it might be her allergies—she does have bad allergies, you know, but she's never felt like this before. The medication he gave her didn't help at all. She's just gotten worse, and I don't know which way to turn. This is not like her. Thank you so much for coming."

"We'll get this resolved. Cindy has all the earmarks of postpartum depression and I think she needs to see her gynecologist tomorrow. We can talk about that tonight."

"Your Aunt Samantha worked her heart out helping this little family. Most of all I was impressed by the depth of love and respect—genuine compassion—she showed to Cindy and Rick as she gave the help. She took Cindy to the doctor and confirmed her own diagnosis. He put her on a different medication and your aunt stayed about two weeks until it kicked in and Cindy began to function again. Then Cindy took the doctor's advice and set up an appointment to see a therapist. He recommended a good one not far from where they lived, a woman who had dealt with these issues for several years. Samantha kept close tabs on Cindy by phone, visiting again about two months later to make her own assessment. Things were much improved and Cindy was back to being the caring mother she had always been before, and feeling much more up to the job."

"She's lucky to have a mother-in-law like that," Lindsey said. "I wonder what Jeff's mother would do if that ever happened to me—and I pray it never will."

"Jeff's mother is a good woman and I have an idea she would rise to the occasion, but you will have a lot to do with that. The reason this worked so well with Cindy and her mother-in-law was because they already had developed a good relationship, which made it possible for Cindy to honestly tell her what was happening and how bad she felt when she called.

"Good relationships are umbrellas in the storms of life," Gigi said. "They may not eliminate the storm, but they sure as the dickens keep it from pouring down on us so hard. Let me show you what I mean by looking in on one of the most beautiful daughter and mother-in-law relationships of all time."

❀❀❀

With Grandma Grace by her side, Lindsey found herself in a strange land, a place she'd never been before. The wind was blowing and the sand was beating upon everything in its path. Palm branches were being whipped and bent low from the power of the wind. It was stifling hot.

"Where are we, Gigi? I can hardly see through the sand storm."

"Look over there," she said, pointing to three women huddled together near a rock alongside a donkey loaded with goods. The women pulled their scarves up around their faces and tucked their long skirts securely under their legs to protect themselves from the stinging pelt of the sand. Gigi and Lindsey came closer so they could hear what the women were saying.

"We will wait here until the wind dies down," the older one said to the others, "then I will continue on to Bethlehem-judah. You must each return to your mother's house in Moab, and may the Lord deal kindly with you, as you have dealt with the dead, and with me. Life can be good for you again."

"Life will never be good again," said one. "Our husbands are dead."

"As is mine for ten years, and then the Lord also took my two sons, your devoted husbands. You are young and will find new husbands and make a new life, and have children to give you joy. I must go on alone to my homeland where I may find a kinsman to care for me."

"Oh, my goodness! This is Ruth and Naomi from the Old Testament! We are actually witnessing their story?" Lindsey said in stunned awe.

"Yes, we are," Gigi said. "Now watch what Naomi does. Seeing it is even more revealing than reading about it."

The wind died down and Naomi took each of her daughters-in-law in her arms and kissed them. And they wept and said, "Surely we will return with thee unto thy people."

And Naomi said, "Turn again, my daughters, why will you go with me? I have no more sons for you to marry. Turn again, my daughters, go your way."

They lifted up their voices and wept again. Orpah kissed her mother-in-law and left; but Ruth wrapped her arms around her and clung to her.

Naomi said, "Behold, thy sister-in-law is gone back unto her people, and unto her gods; return thou after thy sister-in-law."

Ruth said, "Intreat me not to leave thee, or to return from following after thee; for wither thou goest, I will go; and where thou lodgest, I will lodge; thy people shall be my people, and thy God, my God. Where thou diest, will I die and there will I be buried; the Lord do so to me, and more also, if ought but death part thee and me."

Lindsey looked at Gigi and saw tears welling up in her eyes as she said, "Can you even begin to comprehend this kind of love for a mother-in-law? I have so often wondered what happened during the time these young women were married to her sons. Naomi must have treated them with the most tender kind of caring and respect. Love like this doesn't just suddenly happen. Did you notice how she called them 'my daughters.' She was treating them as though they were her very own flesh and blood. She had convinced Orpah to return, but Ruth could not be convinced, and, well, you know the story. She went with her to her homeland. Through a great deal of strategy Naomi found Ruth a husband among her relatives. Ruth married Boaz, and they had a son. Look."

Holding her baby in her arms and with a tender look of love in her eyes, Ruth said to Naomi, "Blessed be the Lord, which hath not left thee this day without a kinsman, that his name may be famous in Israel. And he shall be unto thee a restorer of thy life, and a nourisher of thine old age; for thy daughter-in-law, which loveth thee, hath born him."[20]

"Now I understand," Lindsey said. "All of Naomi's kindness to her daughter-in-law came back to bless her in her old age. Thank you for showing me this beautiful example, Gigi," she said, deeply moved by what she had just seen.

"Like I said, kind and loving in-law relationships can end up being the best kind of insurance policy there is. But most important of all, it's the way to genuine peace; it's true Christ-like living.

"The Pertinent Points I hope you will remember from this window of compassion are: lovingly offer help without trying to own their problems, and wrap your heart around them when they hurt.

"I think it's time we return to my home," Gigi said. "It's the perfect place to begin exploring this next window."

Chapter Ten
Window of Faith

*I*n an instant they found themselves back in Gigi's parlor sitting on her sofa, right where they had started, with the wild flowers still dancing on the computer screen.

"I love your parlor, Gigi. It's so full of unusual charm. A computer to beat all computers, heirlooms and treasures of all kinds, and so many things you've crocheted. Crocheting must be your hobby."

"It keeps me out of mischief. Must have crocheted at least a hundred doilies by now. You do know what a doily is, don't you?"

"Of course, I do. I love this one on the table here. It's lovely," Lindsey said, touching the delicate edges. "Do you have more I could see?"

"Are you serious? I don't know any young person who cares a whit about doilies."

"That would have been me before I met you. But now I really would like to see yours, if you don't mind."

"Well, I'll be," Gigi said. "It will be a pleasure, my dear." She went to a closet and brought out a box full of them.

"We'll just do these few. Don't want to take too much time."

She showed them one by one, identifying the patterns.

"This is such a treat, Gigi. They're all so beautiful."

Holding up the last one, Gigi said, "This is my favorite. It's called Rose Sunburst."

"Oh, it's exquisite!" Lindsey said. "All white and so elegant. Look at the intricate sunburst in the center. And oh, my goodness, it's surrounded with delicate little roses all around the edges. I love roses. How did you do that? Gigi, this is a true work of art. It should be framed and hung on a wall. They all should be. Or in a museum. They're really beautiful."

"Thank you, dear. You've warmed my heart. And now on to our purpose for coming back." She put the box back in the closet and sat down by Lindsey again.

Gigi picked up her Bible from the table, held it close as if caressing it, then laid it on her lap. "Lindsey, I'm going to help you see deep into the window I call faith. And, in case you haven't guessed by now, this will be our guide," she said, patting her Bible.

"Can I hold it, Gigi?" Gigi handed her Bible to her and Lindsey gently ran her hand over the worn leather cover. The gold embossed lettering was still intact, though a bit ragged around the edges. Lindsey opened it to the title page and said matter of factly, "This is the King James Version."

"Oh, yes," Gigi said. "I couldn't think of using any other version, not that I have anything against the others. It's just that the King James is so beautifully poetic, like walking through a flower garden every time I read it. King James' scholars must have been keeping company with Shakespeare. It's my favorite, no question about it. Everyone needs to choose their favorite and then delve into it often. A Bible won't do a lick of good sitting on the shelf collecting righteous intentions."

Lindsey started to give it back to her but she stopped her. "You hold on to it. We'll use it together. I want you to get used to the wisdom inside."

"I'm already familiar with it. I grew up on it."

"I know, and I hope you will never grow out of it. It's meant to be a life-time companion, even for those who didn't have the blessing of growing up with it. They can make friends with it anytime.

"Now on with the window, Lindsey. Do you understand what faith is?"

"I think so. It's believing that God will help us."

"Goes right along with that saying on my wall there." She pointed to the other side of the room. "It's a quote, hundreds of years old, by St. Augustine, a good ole soul who was always searching for the truth. Would you read it for me?"

Lindsey set the Bible on the sofa and walked over to it where she could read the words easily. When she got close she recognized the beautiful Old English style font. *A perfect choice*, she thought. "Where'd you find the quote, Gigi?"

"On the Internet, of course. I heard it years ago, but never knew where to find it. I love this modern technology."

"Me, too," Lindsey said, smiling at the idea of this little old lady being so computer literate. She began reading.

> "Faith is to believe on the word of God, what we do not see, and its reward is to see and enjoy what we believe."[21]

"I especially like that part about 'see and enjoy what we believe,' " Gigi said as Lindsey sat back beside her. "He's basically telling us that having faith means to hold on, and the day will come when we will see and enjoy the fruits of our believing. Sometimes people say 'I'll believe it when I see it,' when, in fact, they'd be a little closer to the truth by saying 'I'll see it when I believe it.'"

"I understand what you mean, Gigi. I saw that several times in the visits we made through the other windows. Many times it was people's faith that got them through the struggles."

"When couples marry," she said, "they need to not only form a partnership with each other, but with God. If He's in on the deal right from the 'Will you marry me?' then many problems, including in-law problems, will be avoided, and those that aren't will be better dealt with because of His influence in the partnership."

"Gigi, you should have been a preacher."

"Missed my calling, I guess. But who needs a pulpit? I'm doing fine without one. Now, how about opening my trusty old Bible to Second Corinthians chapter five verse seven and read it to me."

Following her directions Lindsey found the verse; it wasn't hard because the page was book-marked with a piece of paper. "What's this?" she said, holding up the paper.

"Hold on to it and I'll tell you in a minute. First read verse seven."

"Okay. Here goes, 'For we walk by faith, not by sight.' "

"Soldiers," Gigi said, "do this all the time when they walk into a war zone. They walk by faith, not knowing what's going to happen. If you could have been with our soldiers when they entered enemy territory during Operation Iraqi Freedom you would have seen the evidence of this everywhere. When their lives were on the line they knew where to turn. Chaplains reported that hundreds of these amazingly brave Marines and soldiers of all different religious denominations met together often for prayer in that desert land. In humility they bowed their heads and asked God to be with them and protect them. That paper is an account by one of the chaplains. Now you can go ahead and read it, and as you do try to picture those soldiers in your mind. They're a great example of faith," she said.

Lindsey had seen pictures of soldiers with their heads bowed in prayer, so it wasn't difficult to imagine. In fact, it was very humbling to contemplate. She began reading.

"After all the training, all the physical conditioning hikes, all the strategy sessions, all the intelligence briefs, all the live-fire rifle ranges, it had come to this—a decisive moment and a sincere prayer. We stood together in a circle, asking God for help, for strength, and for courage. . . . In the quiet moments that followed our prayer together, I was reminded, by a voice too deep for words, that we were not alone. Even though we were facing great danger, even though we were about to face our enemies head-on, even though there would be desperate and agonizing hours ahead for all of us, God would be there with us."[22]

"The chaplain went on to tell how those prayers were answered in remarkable, even miraculous ways. Lindsey, we, like these military warriors, need to remember that when we face what may seem like insurmountable problems in difficult relationships, which at times can feel like a war zone, are not alone. It comforts me to know that the good Lord wants us to have peace and to be happy. He wants us to have joy in our family relationships, and that includes with our in-laws. This was His plan, that we be together as families, so we could help and strengthen each other. If that's not happening, we need to turn to Him and say, 'Father, this was Your idea, and I need You.' He loves it when we call on Him. The miracles don't happen unless we ask. Which reminds me, turn to the book of James to chapter four . . . in the New Testament."

"I know. James is one of my favorites. Someone in our Bible study class said that he was Jesus' brother. Is that true, Gigi?"

"Some scholars say so and I don't doubt it, but that's not what we're getting at here. See the last part of verse two, the one underlined in red? Please read it."

"Got it. He said, 'Ye have not, because ye ask not.' "

"Now read the first part of verse three, the underlined part."

" 'Ye ask, and receive not, because ye ask amiss.' Gigi, I don't think I've ever noticed this before. I must have just read right past it. This is pretty significant."

"Yes, it is. Too many prayers never get answered because they never get asked, or when we do pray we sometimes ask for the wrong thing . . . we 'ask amiss.' It's important to pray for the right thing."

"I'm going to show you what I mean by taking you to Lucy's home. Follow me on this because the first part lays the foundation for an in-law situation that happened to them much later. She and Ryan have five children, and one of them, their nine-year-old daughter Amanda, is mentally disabled; they call her Mandy."

"Gigi, sometimes it's scary to me to think about that possibility in my life. A lot of children are born with disabilities. I don't know if I could handle it."

"Most children are born fit as a fiddle. Still, many do come into the world with special challenges; often the challenges are for the benefit of the parents even more than for the child. The way it works out best is for the couple to hold on to each other and to their faith in God. And it helps if parents and in-laws jump in and help out when they can. But back to the story.

"Mandy was presenting her parents with a number of challenges. They loved this little girl and wanted her to enjoy all the happiness of a normal life. In fact, every night they prayed that somehow a miracle would happen and she would be made whole and normal. They knew about the miracles of Jesus and hoped that their faith would bring about just such a miracle for Mandy. After years of praying that prayer they began to feel that the doors of heaven were closed. Mandy never changed, and in fact the difficulties seemed to increase with her age."

"Gigi, sometimes I feel that way, too, like my prayers aren't being heard, like they're going nowhere."

"Well, get that idea out of your head, because I happen to know that every sincere prayer *is* heard. It's just that the answers don't always come in the way we want or when we want, so we think God isn't listening. Trust me, He is," Gigi said sincerely, looking her straight in the eye. "To continue on, one morning while the children were all in school and

Lucy was standing at her kitchen sink something profound happened. In that very spot on that quiet morning the thought came distinctly into her mind that she and Ryan had been praying for the wrong thing for Mandy. What had they been praying for? 'Please make Mandy whole and normal.' Almost as a whispering in her mind, Lucy knew what to pray for. That night when they were preparing to say their nightly prayers, she told Ryan about her experience. Let's look in on them."

She took Lindsey's hand, walked to the computer and clicked the key three times.

Instantly they were in Lucy and Ryan's bedroom. Lindsey was getting used to hanging out in people's bedrooms by now, so it felt pretty natural. Lucy and Ryan took each other by the hand and knelt by the side of their bed.

"Would you like to say the prayer tonight, Lucy?" Ryan asked.
"Yes, I think I would."
They bowed their heads, closed their eyes and she began to pray. "Dear Father, for many years we have asked you to make our Mandy whole and normal. We knew you had the power and we so much wanted her to have all the blessings that normal children enjoy. But now we understand. That is not your plan for her. All these years we have been praying for the wrong thing. We're changing our prayers. Now we ask you simply to bless her with all the happiness that she can enjoy just the way she is. And guide us to know how to help her find that happiness. Thank you for her. In the name of Jesus Christ. Amen."

"Do you see what happened here, Lindsey?"

"They learned to pray for the right thing."

"Indeed they did. They stopped asking 'amiss' and started praying for the happiness that was possible. And little did they know what it would lead to down the road. Many years later a blessing came to Mandy that no one dreamed of, except Mandy. She got married! When she was twenty-seven years old a sweet, kind man named Patrick fell in love with her. He was also mentally challenged, but less than she."

"So was it easier for her to say 'yes' than it is for me?"

"Much easier. He kissed her under a mistletoe, and then said 'I guess this means we're going to get married.' and she said, 'I guess it does.' They were married and now Ryan and Lucy became the parents-in-law of a mentally disabled son-in-law. And it wasn't easy because of the special needs Mandy and Patrick had. Some folks aren't willing to take that on, but because they loved Mandy and knew this marriage would bring happiness to their daughter, they welcomed him into their family and began the process of falling in love with their new son-in-law."

"Did they have children?"

"No. They never could have handled the responsibility, but they had their own little apartment and did their best taking care of each other. Of course, there were problems from time to time, sometimes very serious problems. But Lucy and Ryan looked on the bright side, and enjoyed all the good things they could, including a good laugh now and then."

"What do you mean, a good laugh?"

"Well, one day, for instance, Patrick called their home and Ryan answered," Gigi said as she gestured to a scene in their kitchen.

"Well, hello, Patrick. How are you today?"

"I am so happy," he said. "I finally had one of my life-time dreams come true."

Wonderful," said Ryan. "And what dream was that?"

"At last I own thirty-one pairs of socks!" Patrick said excitedly.

"Well, I think that's terrific. And what is it about that that makes you so happy?"

"What do you mean? Don't you get it? Now I only have to wash my socks once a month!"

"Lucy and Ryan thoroughly enjoyed sharing the amusing things Mandy and Patrick would say. Oh, you gotta hear this one, Lindsey. One Sunday afternoon Mandy called and Lucy answered."

"Hi, Mom. I was just wondering . . . do you ever think about dying?" Mandy asked.

Caught a bit off guard she said, "Well, I guess I've thought about it a time or two. Have you?"

"Yes I have. Have you ever thought about when you want to die?" Mandy was now in a rather somber mood.

"Well, I haven't really thought about it that much. Have you?" she said, starting to get a little worried.

"Yes, I have," she said.

"And when would that be?" Lucy wanted to know.

"Oh, about three o'clock on a Sunday afternoon 'cause there's nothing good on," she said in all seriousness.

"Lucy could hardly wait to tell Ryan about that one. When she told him he said, 'She could then resurrect at seven when the good shows return.' They laughed their heads off over it. They found it very therapeutic to laugh whenever they could. Like the good book says, 'A merry heart doeth good like a medicine.'[23] Keep that in mind, Lindsey. Finding the humor can relieve the tension in all relationships, including with your in-laws. I believe that part of having faith is having a merry heart. And Lucy and Ryan had learned how to do that.

"After Mandy and Patrick had been married about ten years, Patrick's doctor discovered that he was diabetic. Shortly after that his widowed mother passed away and he began to suffer from severe bouts of depression, for which his doctor prescribed medication.

"So you can get a sense of what was happening to Mandy and Patrick let's look in on them."

"What's the matter, Patrick? You seem so sad," Mandy said as she sat down on the sofa next to him.

"You'd be sad too if your mother died," he snapped.

"Don't blame me. I didn't want her to die," Mandy said, incapable of knowing what he really needed.

"Leave me alone," he said as he walked into their bedroom and plopped on the bed.

"Mandy followed him in and said, "Maybe you need to test for your diabetes. Maybe you need some orange juice."

"I don't need anything. Doctors don't know what they're talking about. I don't need to check for anything . . . and I don't need any orange juice either!" he shouted. "I said, leave me alone!"

Mandy walked out of the bedroom, went straight to the phone and called her mother. "Mom, it's Mandy and we've got a problem. Patrick is acting strange, kinda mean. I don't know what to do. I told him it wasn't my fault his mother died."

"Oh, honey. I'm so sorry you're having a problem. Next time maybe you could just be sad with him. I'm sure he misses his mother. Give him a hug when he comes out."

"And he won't do his diabetes testing and he gets mad when I tell him to."

"Now that's serious. I think you need to call his case worker. Maybe she can convince him to do the testing."

"Okay. Bye."

"I love you, bye."

"This was the beginning of a very difficult time in Mandy's life," Gigi said. "Nothing she did or said helped Patrick. It only made him angrier, not only at her but at everyone. His personality seemed to change and he started being verbally abusive to Mandy. Sometimes he would storm out of their apartment and not return until the next day. It was scaring Mandy.

"It was a heartache for Lucy and Ryan to see that their daughter's happiness had changed into her misery. By then they loved their son-in-law and mourned over this change in him. They intervened when they could, though Patrick was determined to handle his problems on his own. Still they showed love to him.

"Again they turned to God and prayed for Mandy to have the strength to do what she needed to do in helping her husband. They prayed for Patrick to somehow be relieved of this terrible illness and to find peace in his life. It was tragic to see him turn into a person so unlike his natural disposition. He took his medication off and on at his own will, which made matters worse. No one knew at the time, but he had also developed pneumonia. One night he and Mandy were asleep in bed, when he sat straight up in the middle of the night and said, "I love you, Mandy. I'm going back to sleep now." When she awoke in the morning he was dead."

"Oh, no! What a terrible shock for Mandy," Lindsey said feeling sad for her.

"Indeed it was; Patrick died of the pneumonia and other complications. Mandy was hysterical. Her parents came as soon as they got word and did their best to comfort her. Patrick's sisters, who lived hundreds of miles away, came and offered their love and sympathy to their bereaved sister-in-law. Listen to this conversation between Mandy and her sisters-in-law, Georgia and Mildred. They were sitting on the sofa in Lucy's home where Mandy was staying temporarily.

"Mandy, I want you to know that we love you and will help you through this," Georgia said.

"We're here for you, Mandy," Mildred said as she put her arm around her.

"Thank you," Mandy said. "But I miss him so much."

"I know. It must be very hard for you. Patrick really loved you," said Georgia. "I remember him calling me after that first date with you. He thought you were real cute."

"He did?" Mandy said, wiping away a tear. "Well, I thought he was real cute, too."

"He was cute and funny. He was always making me laugh," Mildred said, "ever since he was a little kid."

"Yeah, he made me laugh, too" said Mandy. "I remember that time when he dressed up like a monster on Halloween and tried to scare me, then pulled his mask off and said, 'Boo!' Then he laughed so hard he nearly fell over, and so did I." She started to laugh.

"He played tricks on me when we were kids," Mildred said, "And we would laugh like crazy until Mom got mad at us. We had a lot of fun."

They went on like that for some time, just reminiscing the way that only his sisters could do. It definitely helped to cheer up Mandy.

"I can see that the love of these two sisters-in-law made a big difference," Lindsey said.

"Caring in-laws are like a healing balm," Gigi said. "Lucy and Ryan found their own healing balm as they realized that the terrible mental and physical pains Patrick had been experiencing were gone and he was now at peace. Their prayers had been answered, not the way they had hoped, but nonetheless answered in God's way. Now their faith had to really kick in. They did all they could to help Mandy through this difficult time."

"What happened to her?" Lindsey asked.

"She and her parents found great comfort in a certain verse in the Bible. This is one of my all-time favorite passages," she said. "It's Proverbs chapter three verses five and six."

Lindsey knew what to do. She found it and began reading. " 'Trust in the Lord with all thine heart; and lean not unto thine own understanding. In all thy ways acknowledge him, and he shall direct thy paths.' "

"Well done. Now here's the amazing thing, Mandy not only found her own peace, but began to develop in remarkable ways. Oh, she was still as impaired as she had been, but she began to enjoy an unexpected happiness with a kind and caring roommate and involvement in a program for the disabled that was meeting her needs like never before. Let's listen in on Lucy and Ryan several months later."

They were sitting together in their living room.

"I never would have imagined things would work out so well for Mandy after Patrick's death," said Lucy.

"It's like a miracle. God has truly blessed her, and us," said Ryan.

"In more ways than I ever imagined possible," said Lucy. It's amazing how we felt so devastated and sad for her and now we're sitting here marveling at the good life she is enjoying just one year later. "

"And she has sweet memories of Patrick to comfort her," Ryan said. "We were indeed blessed to have had this dear son-in-law in our

lives. Our prayers have been answered for Mandy in so many surprising ways."

"You see, Lindsey, Lucy and Ryan figured out that fret and worry aren't good friends of faith. It's a good thing when people decide that they might as well trust the Lord and be happy with what they have; at least that's my way of thinking."

"Gigi, that makes such good sense."

"It helps, also, to have faith in the goodness of others," Gigi said. "So often good people step up to the plate and hit a home run in our behalf. When you think about it, it's plain to see that God puts a lot of good people on our earthly team."

❀❀❀

"Now," Gigi said, "I'm going to show you an example of how another couple, Daniel and Marie, put this scripture to work in their lives with their son-in-law. I don't know when I've seen a greater act of faith and trust in the Lord than this couple exhibited. Their daughter, Natalie, divorced for several years and the mother of two teenage children, met Josh, also divorced, at her church's singles group. The single men and women of her faith from all over the state where she was living attended these activities. She and Josh had never dated, but were becoming friends when a terrible thing happened to him.

"Josh's exwife had become a drug addict while they were married. He had tried to get help for her, but she didn't want it. In fact, he found out that she was sleeping with the drug dealer. Imagine that!"

"No thanks!" Lindsey said with a grimace.

"Josh did what he had to do, and divorced her. They didn't have any children, but she had two from a previous marriage who lived with their father, thank goodness for their sakes. Anyway, she didn't like the fact that Josh was leaving her, even through she was unfaithful, and did everything to make his life miserable, including sending her drug-dealin' Romeo to harass him. Actually, it was beyond harassment, he threatened bodily harm, even came waving a gun once, and a baseball bat another time. Twice the guy drove right toward Josh as he was walking, almost hitting him with his pickup truck. You never know what people are going to do when they're high on drugs. It was getting pretty frightening. Josh was praying hard to know what to do and at the same time was trying to get some evidence to report to the police.

"By then Josh was back home living temporarily with his single mother, who, I might add for clarity, was a bit on the hysterical side by nature. One day the 'enemy' came banging on Josh's door, shouting some pretty scary stuff. We're going to look in on this scene so you can get a feeling for what he was going through."

"You better open this door or I'm gonna bash your brains out!" he yelled.

Josh's mother screamed, "He's gonna kill us! We've gotta get out of here fast!"

"Quick, Mom, to the garage! Don't worry. I won't let him hurt you." They jumped into Josh's car and quickly drove away. The drug-dealer jumped into his pickup and started to chase them.

"I'm heading for the sheriff's office where we can get some help," Josh reassured her.

"Look out!" she yelled. "He's going to hit us!"

Lindsey and Gigi watched as the guy ran them right off the road. Josh accelerated, trying to get some traction in the gravel so they could get out of there. At this same time the guy jumped out of his pickup and stepped in front of Josh's car as though he was going to attack him. He did this just as Josh got the traction needed to speed up onto the road and make a getaway. His car hit the guy head-on and he fell to the ground.

"Oh, no! I hit him!" Josh said, horrified.

"Keep going!" his mother screamed. "If he's not dead, he'll kill us."

Fearing for his and his mother's lives, he said "No, I won't let that happen."

"Then he sped off to the nearest phone," Gigi said, "where he called the police and the paramedics, then led them to the scene. The guy died in the hospital a few hours later, and, get this, they arrested Josh for murder!"

"No! You're kidding," Lindsey said, finding it hard to believe.

"I don't kid about things like this. To shorten the story, let me just tell you that Josh couldn't afford a good lawyer and the court assigned him a wet-behind-the-ears attorney who didn't have the needed experience. It had to be one of the sloppiest trials in history, with his exwife making all kinds of false accusations. Josh lost his case. The judge banged the gavel and said, 'Fifteen years to life!' Josh was stunned by it all."

"Oh, Gigi, that's terrible! I can't think of anything worse than being sentenced to prison when you're innocent."

Gigi went on with the story. "Natalie was so sad for her friend. He was incarcerated many miles away. She wrote to him often and tried to visit about once a month. Both she and Josh had an abiding faith in God and shared their feelings about this in their letters and during their visits. In the process, she was falling in love with Josh and he with her.

"Her parents, Daniel and Marie, who didn't know Josh, were very concerned."

"I can only imagine how they'd feel," said Lindsey, "their daughter in love with a convicted murderer! How do you deal with that?"

"It scared them half to death. They had heard the story, but weren't sure what to believe about him. They turned to the one source they knew they could count on—God. It came to them that they needed to ask their daughter to do one favor for them before seeing Josh again, which was to go find the minister of the church where he had attended and find out what he knew about Josh."

"What a great idea!" Lindsey said.

"Great ideas have a way of tip-toeing down from heaven when we pray for help. Natalie took kindly to the idea, mostly to pacify her parents, but also to satisfy that little nagging in her own mind. She found the pastor who had known Josh most of his life. Let's look in on that conversation."

The pastor's office was simple—just down the hall from the sanctuary. He was expecting her. On the wall behind his desk hung a painting of Christ. When she entered the room the pastor shook her hand and introduced himself.

"Hello, Natalie. I'm Pastor McKnight," he said, gesturing toward a chair for her to sit and took his place behind the desk. There was something reassuring about seeing that painting above and behind him.

Natalie opened up and explained why she was there. Pastor McKnight leaned forward and said, "Josh is one of the finest men I've ever met. As a kid he never got into trouble, came to church regularly and even gave me a hand with a number of service projects. I took a special interest in him since he was struggling with the death of his father. I've kept my eye on him and he's been an upright citizen in every way. It's a tragedy that this has happened to him."

"He is a good man," Natalie said. "Everything I know about him speaks well of his character."

"I've visited Josh a few times since his sentence," he said. "And every time I come away with an even greater respect for him. There's no question in my mind that he was unjustly condemned."

Gigi went on. "They talked for another thirty minutes about Josh and about God's comforting care. Natalie left feeling like a huge weight had been lifted from her shoulders. At last she was not just going on her own feelings about Josh. Someone she could trust had validated her assessment. She couldn't wait to tell her parents, and to tell Josh what his pastor had said about him."

"So what did her parents do?"

"They felt more at ease about him and even began to visit him on occasion themselves. They liked him right off. Natalie's children corresponded with him and went on some of the visits. Josh had a way with kids and was helping them through some of their own normal teenage difficulties, and in the process *they*, too, were falling in love with him. Daniel and Marie trusted their daughter in the matter. I won't go into detail, but they and many others tried to get a retrial or an early parole, but nothing worked. Josh was a model prisoner, often at risk with other hardened prisoners who called him a goody-goody and did everything to make his life miserable. Thank goodness there were a few 'good' inmates who stood up for him on occasion. It was a terribly trying time for him.

"Well, to get on with it, Josh and Natalie's love was growing stronger and they decided to get married."

"Right there in the prison?" Lindsey said, thinking there couldn't be a worse place for a wedding ceremony.

"Believe me, I absolutely do *not* recommend it. But it happened, right there in the prison, he wearing his prison garb and she wearing, not a typical wedding gown, but a lovely new dress. Her parents, along with his mother, attended the ceremony, giving complete support to their daughter and new son-in-law. Their prayers went up daily in behalf of this new and unique family. They, including Natalie and Josh, were in the heart-and-soul mode of trusting in the Lord completely. We've already learned that answers to some prayers take a long time making their appearance, but to those who keep on praying, the answers finally come, one way or another."

"I think I need to remember that."

"We all do. After seven long years in prison, Josh finally got a parole hearing that was successful. A bright young lawyer, who was on the review board opened everyone's eyes, and in a matter of twenty-four hours from the review Josh was a free man. Of course he was still accountable to a parole officer, but he was free. Natalie, her children and parents shed a bucket full of happy tears. At last Josh could come home and take his place as a devoted husband and loving stepfather."

"Gigi, I'm so happy with this ending!"

"There's no ending until we're six feet under. They still face challenges—big challenges—but through their faith and the faith of their family and in-laws, they're working things out. Now their job is to work hard at loving each other and keep on trusting in the Lord and seeking His little interventions along the way, basically, just like all families need to do."

"But what if it doesn't work out? This is such an unusual case and so much could go wrong," Lindsey said. " What then?"

"Yes, a whole lot could go wrong. When someone spends that much time in prison it can take a terrible toll. It might not work out; that future is yet to be lived. And if it doesn't work then they'll do what they've always done. Pray for guidance and keep on going. That's what we all need to do, keep our faith and keep on going."

❀❀❀

"I want to take you to one more situation before we leave this window. You'll benefit from knowing about Alan and Wanda Blackston and what happened to them. Nobody knows what lies ahead in life and that's why having faith is so important. The Blackston's eldest son, Braden, his wife, Edie, and their three little boys were coming to visit them. The kids were all excited to be visiting their grandparents when a car suddenly veered across the median and struck their van. Braden was killed instantly."

"Oh, Gigi, why do things like this have to happen? I hate it!"

"Well, no one likes it, but it's part of being in a mortal world. Tragic things happen and the happening of them is what helps us draw closer to God, if we rely on Him to help us through. He doesn't cause the problems, but allows them to happen because that's what this world is all about, growing and learning and trusting God, no matter what."

"So what happened to Edie and the children?"

"Edie was injured but recovered completely. The children received only minor cuts and bruises. I'm not going to dwell so much on the tragedy as I am on the relationship between Edie and her in-laws after the accident. It happened several years ago so it gives us a chance to see how things turned out.

"Alan and Wanda had a deep faith in God and it was that faith that sustained them through the loss of their son and helped them develop a loving relationship with their daughter-in-law. As you would expect, the years after the accident were extremely difficult for all of them, but especially for Edie and the children. Braden had been a wonderful husband and a very caring father to their children. He was one of those daddies who played with his kids, helped them with their homework and did so many things to bless their lives. They missed him to the very depth of their souls.

"I feel so sad for the children," Lindsey said. "Even though it's hard, adults can adjust, but how do children make it when they lose a parent like this?"

"Now we're getting to the faith part. Fortunately, these children had been taught that they are children of God and that He loves them. In fact, it had been the tradition of this little family to read scriptures often and have family prayers each evening. These children were given a strong foundation of faith that helped them face this trial. It gave them the confidence that they would see their daddy again someday. Nothing could have helped them through their loss quite like this measure of faith.

"Another thing that helped significantly was the love that surrounded them by family members. When children, or anyone, feel the love of someone else it opens them up to feel the love of God. Now let's explore the in-law relationships this sorrow posed.

"This little family lived a few hundred miles away from their Grandma and Grandpa Blackston, so keeping in touch became a challenge, particularly since their mother was their grandparents' in-law. Alan and Wanda had to maintain a delicate balance, and it wasn't easy at first. They wanted to do everything they could to help Edie raise these dear little children. They wanted to do what Braden would have done. Because Braden had good life insurance, financial needs were not a problem. But certain physical and emotional needs were.

"When they would visit they could see things that needed to be done that weren't being done. Edie was still so involved in licking her own wounds of sorrow that she was somewhat oblivious to the children's needs. Alan and Wanda would try to jump in and help her in kindly ways, but it wasn't taken so kindly."

"It seems to me that she should have appreciated their help," Lindsey said.

"When feelings are involved, and they always are, it's not that simple. Let's look in on them. Alan and Wanda are on their way to visit them again. We'll just slip in the back seat of the car and listen."

"I'm a little nervous about this visit, Alan," Wanda said. "Edie didn't seem real happy with us the last time. What should we do?"

"I'm going to do what Braden would do. I'm going to play with the kids, you know, wrestle them and make them laugh and have some fun, maybe pull a few quarters out of their ears. Things like that."

"While you're doing that I'm going to clean up the kitchen. The last time we were there I couldn't believe how cluttered it had become. I'm sure Edie's still so overcome with grief she just can't do all that needs to be done, so I'll pitch in and do it for her. She's never been a well-organized person and this will give me a chance to show her how to be more organized."

Gigi and Lindsey looked at each other with wide eyes and shaking heads, their lips silently forming the words, "No, no, no. Don't go there, Wanda." Gigi said, "Let's watch how this unfolds. We'll step into this scene two days after the in-laws arrived. It's midmorning. Look, there's Wanda up on a step stool in the kitchen putting a set of mixing bowls away."

Edie, looking forlorn and somewhat bedraggled, still wearing a bathrobe, said, "Mother, please don't put the bowls up there. I need them down here on the cabinet where I can easily find them."

"I'm just trying to help you get things a little more organized. You could use more room on your counter top, so I'm trying to clear a few things away for you, dear. That's all, just trying to help," Wanda replied.

"Please stop. Right now I know where everything is and the last thing I need is to have to wonder where it all went. I know you're trying to help but . . . please, this is not helping."

Stepping down from the stool, with bowls in hand, Wanda said, "But don't you think it would help if things were a little more cleaned up? I know you don't feel up to it and that's okay. I just want to help."

"All it does is help me feel like a bad mother. It's hard enough trying to raise these kids on my own now. I don't need reminders that I'm not doing a good job." With that she started to cry and went back into her bedroom alone and shut the door, leaving Wanda standing there holding the bowls.

Alan walked in carrying the two-year-old on his shoulders. "What's going on?"

"Oh, Alan. I don't know how to help Edie. Everything I do seems to upset her and make matters worse."

He put the child down and put his arms around Wanda. "I know. We just don't fit too well in this house since Braden's death. Still we need to discover what we can do and it may take some time. Let's take Edie and the kids to dinner tonight and clear the air."

"Sounds good." With that Alan went back to entertaining the children and Wanda went out into the back yard where she could be alone and think. She sat down on a lawn chair and did the one thing she always did when she was troubled.

"Dear Father, I need help," she prayed. "I need some guidance here. What can I do to help Edie without offending her?"

"Lindsey, always remember that you can turn to God in any situation and He will help you. Wanda knew this was one of those times for her. He had helped her in the past and she had faith that He would help her now. But Wanda wasn't the only one with faith. Look."

There was Edie, sitting on the side of her bed, making her own plea for help.

"Heavenly Father, I'm making a mess out of all this. My heart is aching so badly and I feel so all alone without Braden that I'm hurting the very people who want to help me most. Please help me to be kinder to them and to know how to be a good daughter-in-law. They're suffering, too. Please forgive me and help me handle this in a better way."

"Gigi, these are all good people just trying to make the best of a terrible heartache."

"Yes, and because of their faith and their desire to help in the best way, they made remarkable strides. It didn't all happen at once, but gradually Alan and Wanda learned to ask Edie what she needed most from them, instead of telling her what she needed. They would offer help, but let it be her decision as to whether or not it was what she wanted."

"That's definitely showing a great deal of respect for their daughter-in-law," Lindsey said. "Mixing respect with faith is a pretty good combination."

"It certainly is. Now here's another point I want to make, Lindsey. There are two kinds of faith. Alan and Wanda learned them both. Not only did they need to have faith in God, but they needed to have faith in Edie and her ability to care for her family. It's been almost eight years since Braden's death and Edie is not only functioning as a capable mother but she welcomes her in-laws into her life with open arms.

"Ah," said Lindsey, "another good twosome: faith *and* patience."

"You got it! We're through here. Let's go home."

❀❀❀

Back in her parlor, Gigi took the Bible, closed it and set it on the table. "Never forget, Lindsey, you can always take your problems to God and He will listen. He won't gossip about them, and He won't betray your confidence as mortals sometimes do. He will always be there for you. And He knows exactly how to nudge someone into action in your behalf. I've often thought that if we could pull back the curtain that separates us from Him, we'd be amazed at how many angels He has in action, just for us . . . just for you."

Then she took Lindsey's hand and tenderly said, "I heard a preacher say something one time that I've never forgotten. 'The obstacles in front of you are never as great as the power behind you.' Rely on that in your relationships with your future husband and in-laws and you'll be just fine."

She couldn't resist giving Gigi a big hug right then and there. And she was hugged back with equal warmth and tenderness.

"So," Gigi said, "my Pertinent Point here is: have faith in God and He will help you through whatever challenges you may face. And have faith in the goodness of the people around you. Together you can make it."

Chapter Eleven
Window of Gratitude

$\mathcal{R}$eady to move on, Gigi said, "The experiences of the many families we've seen leads us naturally into the next window. So to begin let's join a family as they surround their table on Thanksgiving Day."

Three clicks and they were on their way.

"Notice the table setting," Gigi said. "It's their best china, the china that has been passed down three generations. Notice that each plate has a kernel of corn on it. The father, who is sitting at the head of the table is Floyd, and his wife, Dora is sitting at his right. They have five children; three are married. The four littlest ones you see are grandchildren. The older woman is Dora's eighty-year-old widowed mother, Ruby. The whole family is here."

"As you know, the kernel of corn on your plate represents a blessing you will be giving special thanks for this year. Since corn was at the pilgrims' thanksgiving dinner, we honor them by using it as

our symbol," Floyd said. "This year we'll start with Great-Grandma Ruby."

"Thank you," she said. "First of all I'm just mighty thankful to still be alive and kickin' and that I can be with all of you. But that's not the blessing my kernel stands for today. What I'm most thankful for is . . .," she reached in her pocket for a tissue because the tears were already forming, "is for you, Floyd. When Dora married you those many years ago I had no idea that the day would come when you'd be the one showing me the most kind and loving care a mother-in-law could ever hope for. Thank you for being my wonderful son-in-law, and thank you Father above for putting him in my family."

"Now Floyd is needing a tissue, Gigi. Look at that tear on his cheek," Lindsey said.

"He has a tender heart, and it's pushing those tears right out. He loves his mother-in-law dearly."

"Thank you, Mother." He sniffed back the emotion. "I'm the lucky one, as all of us are to have you with us." Feeling a little uncomfortable over the spotlight being on him, he quickly shifted gears. "Okay, we'll just go on around the table now with each of you taking your turn. Zack, you're next."

"Well, I don't know. I guess mostly I'm thankful for turning sixteen and getting to drive," he said.

"And I'm thankful I live in the next county," his older brother said, "so as not to be on the road when Zack's driving." Everyone laughed. "Naw, not really. He's a good kid and I'm going to say I'm just thankful to be his brother."

"Your turn, Johnny."

"I'm thanky for . . . mmmm," the little three-year-old was thinking and playing with his table knife at the same time. He accidently dropped the knife, it hit the edge of his plate and a small chip broke off. He was horrified. A gasp went up from all, knowing the sentimental value of the china. He started to cry, "I'm sorry, Grandma. I broke your special plate."

The boy's parents looked shocked, but before they could do anything Dora was by her grandson's side, putting her arm around him. She said, "It's okay, Johnny. It was an accident. You didn't mean to. Accidents happen. You're much more important to me than this plate, so don't cry, sweetheart. Now what is it you were going to say you're thankful for?"

"I changed my mind. I'm thanky for Grandma didn't get mad at me."

Everyone clapped, and Floyd said, "Good one, Johnny." His mother, sitting next to him, gave him a big hug. Her eyes were full of gratitude as she looked at her mother-in-law. They kept going around the table until it was Dora's turn.

"This is always so hard for me to choose just one blessing because I'm looking at fourteen amazing blessings right here at this table. But I guess I'm going to focus on you, Steven, the newest member of our family. Dixie, you chose well when you married him. Thanks for bringing such a wonderful guy into our family."

"Do you get it why I'm showing you this, Lindsey?"

"I'm beginning to see that this window is all about being grateful and expressing it to your family."

"Including, and maybe especially, your in-laws. And this family knows exactly how to do it. Has everything always run smooth and been rosy for them? No. But they found the key that unlocks the door to family happiness, and that's gratitude. They grew up on it. They know how to say thank you. It reminds me of an old saying, 'A grateful mind is a happy mind.'[24]

❀❀❀

"Let me show you how that worked in another family," Gigi said.

They were in a lovely home that had a warm and inviting feeling about it. Lindsey could feel it as soon as they entered. She couldn't quite put her finger on it; it just felt good being there.

"That's Holly on the phone talking with her son, Kenneth. He's been married almost a year now and they live in a city several hundred miles away. His folks and his wife's parents have always lived right here in Iowa. Holly and Brad are dealing with a bit of a challenge with their daughter-in-law, Brooke."

"Mom, I'm so sorry. I just don't know what to do. Whenever we come to visit, Brooke just insists that we stay at her folks' place."

"It's okay, son. That's not uncommon for a girl to want to stay at her own parents' home. The thing that troubles us is that we don't seem to get you here at our house much at all. We love you and want you and Brooke to at least spend a few hours here. It seems like you just arrive and she's ready to leave."

"I know, Mom, and I want to stay longer, but she always has a reason not to. I don't understand it. I hate to say this, but she says she's just not comfortable there. I love being there with you and the whole situation makes me really sad, but she is my wife."

"Now that's absurd," Lindsey said. "What could be making Brooke uncomfortable here in this wonderful home?"

"See the pictures on the wall?" Gig said.

"Yes, lots of family pictures and a couple of Jesus. I love that one with Him and the little children."

"See that framed cross stitch on the wall?"

"'Love Is Spoken Here.' That's beautiful; such a lovely thought," Lindsey said.

"Brooke didn't grow up in a home like this. Oh, her parents are basically good people, but their values are somewhat different than this family's. Love wasn't always spoken in her home. She feels out of place here."

"She'd love it if she gave it a chance. So how does a mother-in-law deal with this?"

"I'll show you."

They were looking in on Holly's conversation with her husband, Brad, as they sat together eating dinner at the kitchen table.

"Brad, I feel so bad about Brooke. I was so hoping she would feel comfortable in our home and would want to be with us more."

"Me, too. I know Ken wishes things were different. But I'm proud of him for doing what he needs to right now. This is a new little family and they've got to get their feet wet before they can swim," Brad said.

"I see what you mean. They just need a little time to figure it all out without us making it even more complicated," she said.

"I think so. Let's invite them over when they're in town, but not push it. And even if they only stay twenty minutes, let's thank them for coming and tell them how much we appreciate their visit, and not say a word of complaint about feeling bad that they won't stay longer."

"Good idea. We'll just be grateful for whatever portion of their lives they share with us."

"And that's exactly what they did," said Gigi. "They simply enjoyed every minute of Ken and Brooke's visits without complaining that they weren't getting more. Always expressing their love and gratitude. Now let's look in on them three years later."

"Brad, I've got to read you this sweet card Brooke sent." Holly opened it and began reading.

"Dear Mom and Dad, I had to write and tell you how much I enjoyed spending Christmas Eve at your house. Having you read the Christmas story meant so much to me. I never grew up with this tradition, but I want to incorporate it in our home so our children will feel the true meaning of Christmas. I'm so lucky to have married Ken, and to be in your family. Thank you for all the love and understanding you give to us. And thanks for being such wonderful grandparents for our little Mary Jane. I love you, Brooke"

Tears were running down Holly's cheeks as she finished. Brad put his arm around her and said, "Isn't it amazing what a little gratitude, mixed with a big dose of love and patience will do."

"I think our being grateful without being whiny made the difference," she said. "I'm so glad Kenneth married Brooke. She's such a loving, caring daughter-in-law."

"Gigi, I'm also impressed with the gratitude Brooke's showing *them* now."

"When you give a little gratitude it eventually comes back to bless you."

❧❧❧

"I'm going to show you another example you can follow. It's a phone call—a lot of good things can happen on the phone. Cassie is talking to her mother-in-law, Janis."

"Mom, I don't know what I'm going to do about Jayden. We're really worried about him. He's not doing well in school and seems depressed. You know he's on that medicine for his ADD. It was helping before, but it doesn't seem to be doing the job any more. I don't know what to do. I made another appointment with the doctor and will be taking him in next week. The other kids have their own little problems, too, and then there's the struggle of trying to make ends meet. Sometimes I feel so overwhelmed."

"That's got to be hard," said Janis.

"Did you get that, Lindsey? She just listened and understood her daughter-in-law's feelings without telling her even one thing she should be doing."

"I got it. And I can see how well it works, but I'm guessing it takes practice. Giving advice is so automatic," Lindsey said.

"It does take practice, but it's definitely worth it," Gigi said.

"It really is hard, Mom. Did you ever go through times like this?"

"We had our struggles, that's for sure. They weren't quite the same as your's, but there were times I felt completely inadequate for the job."

"Really?"

"Really."

"What did you do to pull yourself out of feeling so burdened?"

"I breathed deep several times and took a bubble bath."

Cassie laughed. "Did it work?"

"It helped, but mostly I just had to plow on through. I called my sister-in-law a lot because she and my brother were my only family in town. She and I shared our troubles with each other two or three times a week. That really helped."

They talked on for a while with Janis mostly listening, then Cassie had to go.

"Mom, thanks so much," she said. "I feel better already just being able to pour it out to someone."

"Thanks for calling. You can pour it out to me anytime you want. I love you, Cassie."

"I love you, too. G'bye."

"There it is again, gratitude being expressed by both of them," Gigi said. "This illustration shows two in-laws saving the day—Janis' sister-in-law many years ago and Cassie's mother-in-law right there and then. What a great gift a caring in-law is.

Lindsey smiled and nodded in agreement.

❀ ❀ ❀

"Now let's do a little fly-by for a quick look at some scenes that show a bit more about how gratitude works," Gigi said . "Look, there. Do you see what's happening?" she asked.

"It's moving day for somebody. I see a big U-Haul truck being unloaded."

"Sybil and Kirk are moving into their new home. Kirk is in the National Guard and was called up for duty two weeks ago, leaving Sybil to do this move on her own, but not alone. See the two guys moving the sofa there? That's her brother-in-law and his friend. See the woman carrying that lamp? That's her sister-in-law. See that young teenage boy? That's another brother-in-law."

"She married a moving crew," Lindsey said.

"She married into a family that cares, is what she did. That's Sybil standing in the hall directing traffic. Listen to what she's saying as they come in."

"I don't know what I'd do without you. Thank you so much. Please put the couch over there by the window." Then seeing the boy coming in with a big heavy box, *"Oh, my goodness! Look at you. You're Superman! Thanks for lending me your muscles. Just set the box over there."*

"She's expressing gratitude," Lindsey said. "And it looks to me like she's got a lot to be grateful for."

❀❀❀

Before Lindsey knew it they were in a different home. A boy about twelve was sitting at the kitchen table with his math book open. Next to him was a young woman, probably seventeen or eighteen years old, checking a problem he had just solved.

"Good job, Charlie! I knew you could do it! Now let's move on to the next problem. Wanna know why they're called problems?"
"It's because they need solving," he said.
"Right on. It's like playing detective in a mystery," she said, saying the word "mystery" with a bit of suspenseful drama. "So, okay, Sherlock, let's solve another one."

"She's tutoring him," Lindsey said, the light dawning. "Is that his big sister?"

"Nope. She's his sister-in-law's sister. If his brother hadn't married who he did, she wouldn't even be in Charlie's life. As it turns out, she's been remarkable in her ability to help him understand math. He was failing, but not anymore. Every time she comes, Charlie's mother expresses gratitude for her help. She's another one of the gifts from heaven. Oh, I love this whole in-law thing!" Gigi said clasping her hands together.

❀❀❀

Next they were on a grassy hillside. A man wearing a plaid kilt was playing the bagpipes—a lullaby. "This is a cemetery!" Lindsey said surprised. "Who died? Oh, no! That's a tiny casket."

"He was only three years old, named Jimmy. Died of a heart defect. The man playing the bagpipes is his uncle. Look at the family."

Gathered around the grave site were people of all ages, some with heads bowed, others looking heavenward, some with tear-filled eyes fixed on the flower-covered casket, as strains of *Danny Boy* filled the air.

"Oh, this is so sad, Gigi."

"Fortunately, the love of heaven descends abundantly on the sorrowing. See the woman with her arm around the younger woman who is holding the hand of her husband? That younger couple, Maria and Thomas, are the parents of the departed little one, and the one with her arm around Maria is her mother-in-law. Maria's own mother passed away a couple of years ago."

"Oh, Gigi, she needs her own mother to comfort her right now."

"Open your eyes just a bit wider and look above them."

Lindsey gasped. Standing just above and slightly behind the couple were two images dressed in white, a woman holding the hand of a small child.

"No one can see them but us," Gigi said. "It's Maria's mother and the dear little boy. I think God took her mother first to be there to welcome the child. And now He's allowing them to be here for this difficult time. Attending spirits can lend great comfort."

The music finished and the woman with her arm around the young mother softly spoke to her.

"I'll be here for you, Maria. I will help you through this."

"Oh, Mother, you have always been here for me. The many sleepless nights you sat by Jimmy so we could get some rest. The many meals you fixed. There are so many things you've already done for us. There's no way to adequately say thank you. I'm so grateful for you. Thank you with all my heart." They embraced each other with tender consoling.

Then Gigi and Linsdey's attention moved to the woman and child dressed in white.

"Jimmy, you don't need to worry about your mama," the woman said, smiling. *"She'll be fine. She has your other grandma to help her*

and your daddy, and they will be happy. And you have me, and I have you. Now that gives me an idea. Shall we ask God if we can be Mama and Daddy's special angels? I think He'll be happy to send us to them when they need some extra comforting. He loves them like we do—even more, if that's possible."

"I would really like that, Grandma. But can I start right now and give Mama a hug?"

"Let's give them both a hug."

Lindsey and Gigi watched as the grandma and boy in white encircled the sobbing mother with their arms, and then encircled the father.

"Oh, Thomas," the young mother said, "do you feel the same loving warmth I'm suddenly feeling?"

"Yes. It's like Jimmy is right here with us . . . maybe even your mother." And they smiled.

"They're angels," Lindsey said feeling humbled by what she had just been allowed to see.

"This family is surrounded by angels, the kind they can see and the kind they can't."

"Maria's mother-in-law is certainly one of them," Lindsey said, feeling like she had just tasted a bit of heaven. "Gigi, families go on forever, don't they." It was a statement more than a question.

"Yes, and Jeff gets it. Didn't he say in his proposal that he wanted you for all eternity?"

"He did. Yes, he did. Family love needs to be so good that we want it to go on forever," Lindsey said.

"It's all in your power to create that kind of love. And, believe me, gratitude plays a powerful role in that process. A woman once told me she had 'the perfect daughter-in-law.' When I asked what it was that made her 'perfect' she said, 'When she's with our family, it's not about her, it's about us. She helps us, she compliments us, she's so pleasant and always expresses appreciation for whatever we do.' You can't help but love a person like that," Gigi said.

"You see," she went on, "when you say thank you to someone you're getting out of yourself and recognizing what someone else has done for you. Love and gratitude go hand in hand. It was Cicero who said, 'Gratitude is not only the greatest virtue, but even the mother of all the rest.'[25]

"I am absolutely certain that the good Lord looks kindly on a grateful heart. Maybe it's time you gave Him thanks, Lindsey, for putting such a good man on your path."

"I *am* grateful, Gigi. And I need to tell Him so."

"Good. To sum it all up, my Pertinent Points here are: Thank your in-laws at every opportunity. Give gratitude to God for the blessing of being an in-law and ask Him to help you do it His way.

"Now to the final window."

Chapter Twelve
Window of Courage

*E*ager to open the final window, Gigi said, "I want to take you to my favorite romantic place. Hold my hand and close your eyes. This is going to be fun,"

When Lindsey opened her eyes they were sitting under a cluster of swaying palms near a turquoise-blue ocean, with the waves gently rolling onto a white sandy beach.

"This has to be Hawaii, Gigi!"

"Maui to be exact. No place I'd rather be when I want to relax and clear my head."

"I've never been to Hawaii, but I've always wanted to go."

"Well, then, it's time you and Hawaii got acquainted. Don't talk, just look and drink it all in."

They sat there for a time mesmerized by the rhythmic sound and motion of the foam-capped waves. Wispy white clouds spotted the azure blue sky. A couple, hand in hand, came strolling along the beach, allowing the waves to wash across their bare feet. Her long dark hair, decorated by a bright pink flower above her ear, caught the tropical breeze. He put his arm around her shoulders and drew her closer as she put her arm around his waist. They didn't seem to be saying anything, just smiling as they walked.

"I'm betting they're on their honeymoon," Lindsey said.

"You're talking."

"Oops. Sorry."

They stayed there for awhile, just observing the beauty that surrounded them. Then Gigi stood up, and Lindsey followed her lead. They walked along the beach for several yards and rounded a bend where Gigi led her to a path that took them inland. They walked for some time, taking in all the various shapes and shades of the lush, green foliage and beautiful tropical flowers. Then suddenly Lindsey's breath was taken away by what she saw—a picture-perfect waterfall cascading down a rocky cliff, splashing into a deep-blue pool. It was a virtual paradise.

She thought they were alone, then noticed a couple who were lying in a hammock between two palm trees. His arm was under her neck with his hand resting on her bare shoulder. They were in swim suits with a large beach towel draped across the lower part of their bodies. His slightly-graying hair and the gentle wrinkles at the corners of her eyes and mouth led Lindsey to think they could be in their mid fifties.

"See that couple there?" Gigi asked, nodding in their direction.

"You're talking," Lindsey said.

"I'm in charge. Quiet time is over and learning time has arrived. Listen to what they're saying."

"Can you believe we've been married thirty-five years?" he said in a reminiscent mood.

"It doesn't seem possible, but on the other hand I can hardly remember when we weren't. Here we are, four kids and five grandchildren later," she said.

"Seems weird to be lying here in Hawaii next to a grandma," he joked.

She sat up slightly, looked at him and sternly said, "Would you like to rephrase that?"

"Uh . . . lying here in Hawaii next to this beautiful woman who happens to be the grandmother of the cutest kids this world ever saw," he said with a twinkle in his eye.

"Now you're talkin', Grandpa," she said, and kissed him passionately. Then she laid back down against his arm.

"Gigi, that's the kind of marriage I want."

"I know, but it requires getting married first, you know, saying yes. And that's where you're stuck."

"I'm not nearly as stuck as I was before I met you. But I still have this little fear about taking such an important step."

"What are you afraid of?"

"I want to be sure I've found the right guy, with the right family, the right goals, the right personality, the right faith, the right career, the right . . ."

"Hey, wait a minute. You sound like some kind of perfectionist when it comes to who you'll marry. Get off that. Stop being a perfectionist and just be a close-enough-ist. Mr. Perfect doesn't exist, and neither does Miss Perfect."

"I'm sure that's true."

"So, is Jeff close enough?" Gigi asked.

"I'd say he's really close."

"Do you love him?"

"Oh, yes. I do love him. And I know now I can deal with the in-law challenges. But it's just that . . ."

"That you're scared by the statistics," Gigi said. "Too many divorces happening." She knew.

"I don't want that to happen to me. One of my best friends is divorced after only one year of marriage," Lindsey said.

"I have to tell you, Lindsey, that really upsets me— young people divorcing at the drop of a hat over the most ridiculous things. People get divorced now for what most couples go through naturally on their way to the good times. And they miss out on the best part. It's really very sad. Of course, there are valid reasons for divorce, but too many fit this category. Marriage takes courage. That's why we're here at this window."

"This must be the window of courage."

"That's right. Taking the big step into marriage is a leap of courage and a willingness to make a life-long commitment. Have you got what it takes? Are you ready to leap?" she asked her point blank.

Lindsey turned away. "Am I ready?" she asked herself. Then she looked at the couple in the hammock again.

"I'm so glad I married you, Don," she said. "What if I had said no when you . . . I'll never forget that afternoon when we sat there by the river. You pulled the ring out of your pocket and just simply said, 'Will you marry me?' What if I had said no? It would have been a terrible mistake. I love you so much."

"And I love you, too, sweetheart. It hasn't been easy and we've been through a lot, but oh, has it ever been worth it," he said kissing her tenderly.

"We thought we were in love then, but it doesn't hold a candle to what we have now," she said.

"And I have a feeling that it's only going to keep getting better."

"We'll just have to keep coming to Hawaii to make sure," she said with a playful grin.

❀❀❀

"Lindsey, I'm going to show you one more scene to help you make up your mind," Gigi said.

Before she knew it they were standing at a hospital nursery window, along with a couple of women—"pink ladies," caring older women who volunteer to help out. The nursery had five tiny new babies on display, probably waiting for their daddies to come by and show them off to relatives. Boys had blue cards with their names displayed and girls had pink ones.

"Oh, Gigi, look at that little baby girl with that tiny pink ribbon tucked into her curly black hair. She's so adorable. And look at that cute little one with the chubby cheeks with a ribbon stuck on her little bald head. And there's a boy, see the one with the brown hair—he's looking tough already. They're all so cute!"

"I always love to visit the nursery," Gigi said. "These little ones are God's witness that the world will go on and will be filled with love. See that little blond fellow there, I'd like to give him a great big hug. He reminds me of one of my boys. Oh, how I loved that little guy! However, our real purpose in coming here is to listen to the conversation these pink ladies are having."

"Don't you just love to look at these new babies, Gladys?" one said to the other.

"Yes, I often come up here to . . . well, dream, I guess."

"Me, too. It reminds me of when I had my own little ones. Twins. What a happy day that was for me and my husband, may he rest in peace. Now my children are all grown up and I've kinda switched places with them. They're taking care of me—well, not totally, but they do come by and make sure I'm fine and bring the grandkids, and well it's wonderful. I think it's nature's way of saying thank you for bringing them into the world. How many children do you have?"

"Actually, I don't have any. I never married. I wanted to, but well . . ."

"What happened? Do you mind my asking?"

"No, I don't mind. What happened was I think I was just too particular and a little afraid of . . . this is silly, I know, but the truth

is I was afraid of having in-laws. My sister had a really weird mother-in-law and it scared me off. I was dating a great young man, but was afraid I wouldn't get along with his mother. He asked me to marry him, but I kept putting him off. While I was trying to decide he met someone else and married her. He was a good man. Oh, how I wish I had said yes. I never seemed to find the right guy. I guess I was just too picky, and ended up missing out on so much."

"I'm so sorry," the other woman said, putting a comforting arm around her friend.

"That's it, Gigi. I've seen enough. I'm ready. I can see that a person could go through life cautiously wondering and miss the whole grand finale. I'm ready! I'm going to say yes to Jeff," she said with absolute resolve.

Suddenly they were back at the waterfall.

"If you brought me to Maui to clear my head, all I can say is, it worked."

"Well, thank goodness! Look, Lindsey," Gigi said pointing to the waterfall where the rays of the sun reflected off the water.

"Oh, a rainbow! It's beautiful."

"I think God just smiled on your decision," Gigi said with a nod and a victorious smile of her own.

Just then Lindsey heard a dog bark. She jerked.

"What? Where am I?" She looked around, confused. "Where's Hawaii? Where's Gigi?" Then she realized she was sitting on the bench across from the Victorian row houses. She jumped up, looked at the houses searching for the

Grandma Grace sign. There was no sign, just a dog racing off down the street.

"But it was so real," she said right out loud. "So incredibly real!"

In somewhat of a stupor she started walking to her hotel. As she walked she felt something in her pocket, reached in and pulled out a card. It said, "To everything there is a season, and a time to every purpose."

She turned the card over and on the back it said: "He shall give his angels charge over thee, to keep thee in all thy ways. Psalm 91:11."

Lindsey suddenly felt warm all over. She looked up and repeated the words, "He shall give his angels charge over thee." She smiled. Putting her hand in her other pocket she found a piece of paper with a website on it. "I think I just might need this," she said, smiling again. This was her season.

Then she realized she needed to get busy, and she had to be quick about it. Her heart started racing and so did her steps. Her plane didn't leave until 11:00 the next morning so she had some time to plan her answer.

Back at the hotel she looked at Jeff's proposal again. The monkey took the lid off and there was the ring. An idea popped into her head. She had to hurry if she was going to pull it off. She took out her cell phone and dialed a number.

"Hello, Blake? This is Lindsey. I need you to do me a big favor," she said to her cousin's husband back home. She knew she could count on him, he's a real ham. Then it occurred to her, in-laws, even cousins-in-law, are nice to have. They talked for a few minutes and he was more than happy to oblige.

The next morning, while she was on her way to the airport, Blake did exactly as she had outlined. He appeared at Jeff's studio in a black tux with tails, white shirt and bow tie with a white towel draped over his arm, looking like one of the fanciest maitre d's you ever saw. He was carrying a crystal platter with a silver domed lid.

"Is Mr. Jeffrey Sloan here, please?" he said in a snobbish sort of way.

The woman at the desk smiled and took him back to where Jeff and several other students were working on a project. She pointed to Jeff. Blake walked over to him, pulling the whole charade off to a tee.

"Mr. Sloan, I presume?" he said in his high and mighty voice.

"Yes, that's me," Jeff said, more than a little surprised.

Bringing the tray out from behind his back he said, "Your answer, sir."

Jeff jumped up out of his seat, jerked off the lid and there was an envelope that said, "Don't open this until you see me at the airport at 2:00 this afternoon. Pick me up at baggage claim. Thanks. Lindsey."

Blake left with the props, leaving Jeff holding the envelope. He held it up to the light, but couldn't read the contents. He put it in his pocket and tried to get his mind back to work. Lindsey wasn't about to let him know her answer without being with him.

The other students there had helped him make the DVD so they knew about the proposal and teased Jeff all morning. Finally, it was time to leave for the airport. He drove so fast it's a wonder he didn't get a ticket, as if getting there sooner would make her arrive faster.

As soon as Lindsey left the plane she walked as fast as she could, almost running, to the escalator leading to baggage claim. There he was, waving the envelope when he saw her.

Neither of them could wait. He ripped it open as soon as she was by his side. On the paper was one word. YES!

"She said yes!" he shouted to everyone in the baggage claim area. "She said yes! She's going to marry me!"

He threw his arms around her and they kissed exuberantly. Everyone started clapping and shouting "Congratulations!" It was the most wonderful kind of pandemonium you could imagine. Lindsey couldn't help wishing Gigi could have been there.

Epilogue

$\mathcal{I}$t was a lovely wedding. Lindsey looked stunning in her white satin wedding gown with white embroidered flowers delicately decorating the front and cascading down the train. Her hair was swept up in the back into a cluster of curls with a shoulder length veil flowing from beneath. She was indeed a beautiful bride.

Loved ones and close friends seemed to come out of the woodwork to attend. After the ceremony everyone went to Jeff's mother's home for a garden luncheon. It was late Spring and everything was in bloom. Tables were set up all over the yard and people were milling about making their selections from the buffet table and visiting. Jeff's mother had gone all out. She wanted to have this wedding luncheon at her home. Lindsey's parents were giving them a reception later that evening. It pleased her to see how both parents worked things out in harmony. She was thankful for what she had learned and put it to use many times during the planning sessions. The luncheon was perfect. People were not only giving them gifts but all kinds of good wishes and advice.

At one point, when most of the guests were finally seated, Blake stood up and tapped his goblet with his knife to get everyone's attention.

"Ladies and gentlemen," he said putting his napkin over his arm and assuming his high and mighty waiter voice and posture, "I would like to make a toast to the bride and groom. May your life be filled with silver-domed dishes full of wonderful surprises beneath the lid."

"Hear, hear!" shouted someone and they all clapped. A few more well wishers made toasts, and then Jeff stood up.

"I have waited for this moment to tell Lindsey, my beautiful bride," he looked at her adoringly, "where I'm taking her for our honeymoon. I wanted to keep it a surprise until now."

He took her hand and had her stand by him as he handed her an envelope.

"Open it," he said, with a big smile he couldn't contain.

She eagerly did, and inside was a brochure.

"Oh, Jeff, we're going to Hawaii?"

"That's right. You've always wanted to go. And we're staying in Maui right near this beautiful spot," he said, pointing to a picture inside the brochure. She caught her breath and could hardly believe her eyes. There it was. The waterfall, the blue pool, even the hammock!

"How did you know?" she said, overwhelmed with joy.

"Know what? I just knew you wanted to go to Hawaii and we're going!"

She threw her arms around him and kissed him and kissed him and kissed him. What a great surprise this was. Everyone applauded again.

After most of the guests had gone, Jeff and Lindsey went in the house to relax a bit and open a few remaining gifts. Jeff's mother was sitting on the sofa in the living room, looking a little exhausted, but happy. Lindsey went right to her, sat down beside her, hugged her warmly and said, "Thank you, Mother, for all you've done, and for giving us this wonderful party."

Sarah smiled back and said, "You're so welcome, dear. It's been a joyful time for me. You've brought a new light into our family."

"Thanks for that. You need to know that I'm really happy to be in your family," Lindsey said, squeezing her mother-in-law's hand.

"Okay, time to open a few more presents," Jeff said, joining them.

After the last gift was opened, Lindsey stood up to stretch and excused herself. As she walked down the hall she noticed an open door to a room she had never been in before. It was filled with family photos all over the walls and on tables. It must have been the room where Jeff's mother did her scrapbooking. She was drawn irresistibly into the room, and started looking at the photos on the wall. She gasped.

Jeff had followed her in and said, "What's wrong?"

"I know her," she said pointing to one of the old photos. "I've seen her before. Who is she?"

"That's my father's aunt. He adored her. She lived a long way from us. I only met her a couple of times when I was a little boy and she was really old. Still I remember her as being a very kind lady, a little on the spunky side, but very kind."

"Did her name happen to be . . . Grace?" she timidly asked.

"Yes, it was. In fact everyone, and I mean everyone, called her Grandma Grace."

Lindsey was shocked beyond words.

"What's the matter?" Jeff asked.

"I'll explain it to you someday."

Just then Jeff's mother entered the room.

"Oh, here you two are," she said.

"I just introduced Lindsey to Grandma Grace," he said.

"She was amazing," his mother said.

"Amazing Grace," Lindsey said remembering a window.

"Sometimes we actually called her that," his mother said. "After her children were grown she finished her college degree and went into counseling, even had a little radio show at one time."

"I knew that was her voice," Lindsey said softly to herself.

"Oh, that reminds me," Jeff's mother said as she went to the closet. She found a gift on the shelf and handed it to Lindsey.

"This is for you. I almost forgot."

The card on the box said, "For Jeff's wife."

"She left gifts, heirlooms actually, for all her grandchildren and nieces and nephews—even the greats," his mother said, "to be given at their weddings. She knew she'd be long gone before most of them."

Lindsey opened the card. Inside it said, "With love from Grandma Grace." Then at the bottom in smaller letters it said, "But you can call me G. G."

Lindsey was astounded. She carefully removed the paper and opened the box. She couldn't believe her eyes. It was . . . the Rose Sunburst doily. She touched it almost reverently, then gently picked it up and held it to her heart. She began to cry, and no one knew why.

"Thank you, Gigi," she said softly. "Thank you, for everything."

The End

Grandma Grace's Pertinent Points for Happy In-law Relationships

♥ Know the heartaches of their past so you can love them in the present.

♥ Open your ears more and your mouth less.

♥ Put yourself in the other person's shoes and see how it feels.

♥ Build a sure foundation by setting boundaries kindly

♥ Give up grudges and be a white-flag waver.

♥ Let forgiveness be your best friend.

♥ Be willing to wait patiently for a good relationship to happen.

♥ Give them time to grow into who they are in the process of becoming.

♥ Love them just the way they are, differences and all

♥ Don't play favorites.

♥ Be their friend, not their boss or their slave.

♥ Honor their right to make their own choices without being offended.

♥ Keep your nose out of their private business and theirs out of yours.

♥ Lovingly offer help without trying to own their problems.

♥ Wrap your heart around them when they hurt.

♥ Have faith in God and He will help you through whatever challenges you may face.

♥ Thank your in-laws at every opportunity.

♥ Give gratitude to God for the blessing of being an in-law and ask Him to help you do it His way.

Send us a letter

*D*ear Reader,

We hope you enjoyed reading *Meeting Amazing Grace.* Now that you've read it we would like to hear from you. Please share your thoughts and ideas by emailing us at gjlundberg@gmail.com.

Thank you.

Gary and Joy Lundberg

Reference Notes

Chapter 2

1   . Old Testament, Proverbs 9:12
2   . William Shakespeare, *The Tragedy of Hamlet Prince of Denmark*, The Harvard Classics, 1909, p. 14

Chapter 3

3   . Gary and Joy Lundberg, *I Don't Have to Make Everything All Better*, Penguin Group, 1999, p. 199
4   . William J. Doherty, Ph.D., and Barbara Z. Carlson, *Putting Family First*, Henry Holt and Company, NY, NY, 2002, p. 138

Chapter 4

5   . See Joanne C. May, *Family Attachment Narrative Therapy: Healing the Experience of Early Childhood Maltreatment*, Journal of Marital & Family Therapy, July 2005, Vol. 31, Number 3, p. 223
6   . The Five Step program was formulated by Lynne Jay Lundberg, Ph.D., St. George, Utah, used by permission.
7   . Neal A. Maxwell, *Meek and Lowly*, Deseret Book, Salt Lake City, 1987 p. 7.
8   . New Testament, Matthew 18:21-22
9   . Matthew 6:14
10 . New Testament, Matthew 5:9

Chapter 5

11 . Old Testament, Proverbs. 37: 7
12 . New Testament, Hebrews 12:1

Chapter 6

13 . Psalms 30: 5

14 . Hebrews 8:12

15 . Dept. of Health and Human Services, Centers for Disease Control and Prevention
http://www.familyresearchinst.org/FRI_EduPamphlet3.html

16 . New Testament, Matthew 5:4

Chapter 7

17 . Old Testament, Exodus 20:12

18 . See Rick Warren, *The Purpose Driven Life*, Zondervan, Grand Rapids, 2002, pp. 193-216

19 . New Testament, John 13:34

20 . Old Testament, Ruth Chapters 1 - 4

Chapter 10

21 . St. Augustine, *New Dictionary of Thoughts*, Standard Book Company, USA, 1961, p. 199

22 . Lt. Carey H. Cash, *A Table in the Presence*, W Publishing Group, a Division of Thomas Nelson, Inc., Nashville, 2004, p. 23-25

23 . Old Testament, Proverbs 17:22

Chapter 11

24 . Secker, *The New Dictionary of Thoughts*, Standard Book Company, USA, 1961 p. 246

25 . Cicero, *The Christian Leader's Golden Treasury*, Droke House, Indianapolis, 1955 p. 237

Acknowledgments

*T*his book has been like a bee gathering nectar. Every time the manuscript landed in the hands of an editor, a friend or family member it became richer and more polished. We thank you all, but especially Darla Isackson, Kaye Hanson, Ester Rasband, and Cleo Saunders, who made significant editing contributions. Others who read the manuscript and gave ideas and encouragement to see it through to publication are Doro Bush Koch, Janice Kapp Perry, Carla Call, Shawna Powelson, Sandy Willis, Deb Richards, Fern and Soren Cox, and several other devoted readers. Thank you! Your help and encouragement made all the difference.

We sincerely thank the many who shared their personal stories, but must remain anonymous. You'll know who you are when you recognize yourselves in the different scenarios. You are the heart of this book and we thank you for sharing that others may learn and find the courage and desire to pursue happy relationships in their own families.

We are most grateful to our dear family members who have shared their love and wisdom and have been great examples of the concepts presented in this book.

We thank Jana Parkin for using her superb artistic talent in creating such an inviting cover for our book. She has blessed our lives once again.

Finally, we humbly thank God for inspiration that we sought for daily during the writing. We believe that ". . . with God all things are possible." (Matthew 19:26) We are grateful for His influence throughout the creation of *Meeting Amazing Grace*.

Keynotes, Seminars and Workshops

Gary and Joy Lundberg speak at events for business, civic, and church groups. Their subjects vary from improving communication on the job, to setting effective boundaries, to creating happy marriage and family relationships. Presentations and addresses are tailored to your specific needs. For more information about the Lundbergs visit their website at www.lundbergcompany.com.

You can contact them at 1-800-224-1606 or email at gjlundberg@gmail.com.